Mathematics
for Key Stage Three

Hundreds of practice questions and worked examples
covering the Key Stage Three Maths curriculum.

Book One

Contents

Number

Section 1 — Numbers and Arithmetic

Section 2 — Approximations

Section 3 — Powers

Section 4 — Multiples, Factors and Primes

Section 5 — Fractions and Percentages

Ratio, Proportion and Rates of Change

Algebra

Section 12 — Graphs and Equations

Geometry and Measures

Section 13 — Angles and Shapes

Section 14 — Constructions

Section 15 — Perimeter, Area and Volume

Section 16 — Transformations

Probability

Section 17 — Probability

Statistics

Section 18 — Statistics

Throughout the book, the more challenging questions are marked like this:

Editors:

Katherine Craig, Shaun Harrogate, Ceara Hayden, David Ryan, Sophie Scott, Caley Simpson, Ben Train, Dawn Wright

Contributors:

Rosemary Rogers, Kieran Wardell

Reviewers:

Mona Allen, Peter Caunter

Proofreaders:

Simon Little, Rachael Marshall and Charlotte Whiteley

Published by CGP

ISBN: 978 1 78294 162 0

Clipart from Corel®

Printed by Elanders Ltd, Newcastle upon Tyne.

Based on the classic CGP style created by Richard Parsons.

Section 1 — Numbers and Arithmetic

1.1 Place Value and Ordering Numbers

Place Value

You can split numbers up into columns.
The <u>digit</u> in each column tells you how many of each thing you have:

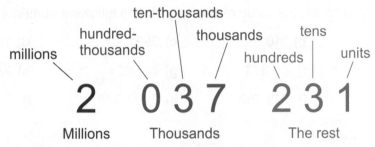

Big numbers are written with their numbers in groups of three, where each group
shows millions, thousands, etc. This makes large numbers easier to read.

Example 1 Write down the value, in words and as a number, of each digit in 2 730 491.

Write down how many you have in each column.

Then write each digit...	...in words...	...and as a number.
1 unit	one	1
9 tens	ninety	90
4 hundreds	four hundred	400
0 thousands	zero	0
3 ten-thousands	thirty thousand	30 000
7 hundred-thousands	seven hundred thousand	700 000
2 millions	two million	2 000 000

Exercise 1

1   For each of the following numbers, write down in numbers the value of the digit in:

i) the tens column   ii) the thousands column   iii) the hundred-thousands column

a) 1 283 458   b) 2 432 042   c) 7 263 982   d) 8 008 761

e) 9 920 675   f) 6 309 183   g) 3 792 023   h) 4 802 811

i) 7 865 201   j) 9 210 399   k) 1 621 307   l) 5 759 034

2 Write down the value of the underlined digit in the following numbers:

  i) as a number   **ii)** in words

  a) 5 2<u>3</u>1 099   **b)** <u>8</u> 279 708   **c)** 3 954 <u>0</u>28   **d)** 5 112 3<u>8</u>2

  e) 7 44<u>3</u> 028   **f)** 4 00<u>8</u> 271   **g)** 1 <u>4</u>95 221   **h)** 2 1<u>9</u>2 110

  i) 6 926 77<u>3</u>   **j)** 3 302 <u>2</u>89   **k)** <u>6</u> 828 362   **l)** 8 3<u>5</u>2 447

3 Write down, in numbers, the value of each digit in the following numbers.

  a) 203   **b)** 810   **c)** 3921   **d)** 1987

  e) 63 291   **f)** 80 373   **g)** 797 634   **h)** 28 977

  i) 921 337   **j)** 818 752   **k)** 2 871 354   **l)** 7 620 931

| **Example 2** | **Write the amount £4829309 in words.** |

1. First, split the number up into groups of three.
   Start on the right-hand side
   of the number and move left,
   putting a space every three numbers.   £4 829 309

2. Then read each group from left to right.   £ 4 million, 829 thousand, 309

3. Write the number out fully in words.   **Four million, eight hundred and twenty nine thousand, three hundred and nine pounds.**

Exercise 2

1 Write each of these numbers in words.

  a) 15298   **b)** 40291   **c)** 82179   **d)** 74331

  e) 23005   **f)** 25221   **g)** 10281   **h)** 55501

2 Write each of these numbers in words.

  a) 452123   **b)** 605128   **c)** 391407   **d)** 515398

  e) 933148   **f)** 295341   **g)** 709382   **h)** 351922

  i) 121445   **j)** 678144   **k)** 366121   **l)** 892153

3 Write each of these numbers in words.

a) 1163720   b) 2810278   c) 6201827   d) 7277260

e) 6271029   f) 4482910   g) 1009275   h) 5997165

i) 1321992   j) 7392014   k) 9371720   l) 5009801

m) 8109200   n) 6211315   o) 8900003   p) 1628102

4 Write each of these values in numbers.

a) Twelve thousand, three hundred and ninety-seven.

b) Eight hundred and seventy-four thousand, two hundred and nine.

c) Six million, one hundred and sixty-three thousand, five hundred and eleven.

d) Four million, seven hundred and thirteen thousand and nine.

5 Harriet is filling out a cheque for £9703109. What is this amount in words?

6 Benjamin is writing a cheque for £88600531. What is this amount in words?

Investigate — Place Value in Decimals

As with whole numbers, decimal numbers can be split up into columns called decimal places:

units   tenths   hundredths

$$1.73$$

a) Look at the number. The first two decimal columns are labelled. Use what you know about the names of the columns in whole numbers to label the column that would come next.

b) Think about the number 1.7324. What would you call the column that the 4 is in?

c) Write out a number with 5 decimal places and label each column.

d) How many decimal places would a number with a digit in the 'millionths' column have? Write out a number with a 'millionths' column.

e) What is the value of the 3 in the number 0.0000003 in words?

f) Write out some more decimal numbers. Find the value of each digit in each one.

Ordering Numbers

a) Which amount is larger, 1201 kg or 1210 kg?

Compare the digits in each number column by column, moving left to right, until one has a larger digit than the other.

1. Start by comparing the number in the thousands column: 1201 and 1210 both have 1 thousand

2. Compare the digits in the hundreds column: 1201 and 1210 both have 2 hundreds

3. Compare the digits in the tens column: 1201 has a 0 in this column. 1210 has a 1 in this column, so is larger.

4. You can use the < or > signs to show which number is bigger. The wide end of the symbol goes next to the larger number: **1201 kg < 1210 kg**

b) Put the two masses onto the number line shown.

1. Work out what each dash on the number line represents. There are **10** spaces between 1200 kg and 1210 kg.
So each dash represents:
$(1210 - 1200) \div 10 = 10 \text{ kg} \div 10 = 1 \text{ kg}$

2. Write the masses on the number line in the correct places.

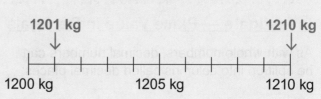

Exercise 3

1 Use the < and > symbols to show which amount in each pair is larger.

a) 16 kg , 61 kg **b)** 94 s, 98 s **c)** 54 g, 45 g **d)** 91 ms, 97 ms

e) 186 ml, 168 ml **f)** 212 cm, 218 cm **g)** 336 g, 332 g **h)** 721 m, 712 m

2 Use the < and > symbols to show which amount in each pair is larger.

a) 1665 m, 1766 m **b)** 1108 kg, 1208 kg **c)** 1302 m, 1392 m **d)** 9302 ml, 9120 ml

e) 6251 s, 6250 s **f)** 8006 ml, 8010 ml **g)** 1312 g, 1310 g **h)** 2221 kg, 2220 kg

i) 8910 m, 8911 m **j)** 5200 s, 5201 s **k)** 7721 kg, 7228 kg **l)** 2188 m, 2186 m

3 Write each set of numbers on a copy of the number line shown.

a) 98, 97, 79

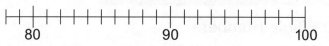

b) 75, 55, 77

c) 192, 198, 182

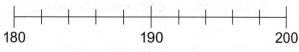

d) 298, 303, 301

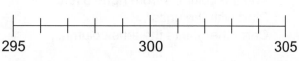

e) 5262, 5226, 5254

Example 4 **Put the following numbers in order from smallest to largest:**
68,   128,   487,   26,   1921,   1829,   287,   3

1. Sort the numbers into groups based on how many digits they have.

1 digit	2 digits	3 digits	4 digits
3	68	128	1921
	26	487	1829
		287	

2. Then put each group in order by comparing the digits in the columns, going from left to right.

Increasing size ⟶

3	26	128	1829
	68	287	1921
		487	

3. Write out the full list in order.

3, 26, 68, 128, 287, 487, 1829, 1921

---

4 Write these sets of numbers in order from smallest to largest.

a) 61, 67, 76, 62, 55, 70

b) 42, 44, 60, 4, 58, 56

c) 52, 25, 5, 22, 2, 50

d) 112, 132, 110, 100, 111, 131

e) 162, 182, 172, 77, 180, 167

f) 77, 176, 171, 172, 161, 69

5 Write these sets of numbers in order from smallest to largest.

a) 7161, 7511, 620, 51, 665, 621, 49, 734

b) 182, 889, 1882, 18, 84, 1880, 8, 6

c) 6, 90, 68, 1921, 6621, 6667, 9, 66

d) 163, 3, 1921, 662, 31, 1633, 166, 168

1.2 Addition and Subtraction

Adding Whole Numbers

| Example 1 | Work out 1129 + 238. |

1. Write out one number above the other, making sure the units columns line up.

$$\begin{array}{r} 1\ 1\ 2\ 9 \\ +\ \ \ 2\ 3\ 8 \\ \hline \end{array}$$

2. Add the columns from right to left. Start with the units. $9 + 8 = 17$ Carry the '1' into the tens column.

$$\begin{array}{r} 1\ 1\ 2\ 9 \\ +\ \ \ 2\ 3\ 8 \\ \hline 7 \\ {}_1 \end{array}$$

3. Now add up the tens column, including the 1 carried over. $2 + 3 + 1 = 6$

$$\begin{array}{r} 1\ 1\ 2\ 9 \\ +\ \ \ 2\ 3\ 8 \\ \hline 6\ {}_17 \end{array}$$

4. Do the same with the hundreds column. $1 + 2 = 3$

$$\begin{array}{r} 1\ 1\ 2\ 9 \\ +\ \ \ 2\ 3\ 8 \\ \hline 3\ 6\ {}_17 \end{array}$$

5. When you get to the thousands column, there's no adding to do — so write the number straight into the answer.

$$\begin{array}{r} 1\ 1\ 2\ 9 \\ +\ \ \ 2\ 3\ 8 \\ \hline 1\ 3\ 6\ {}_17 \end{array}$$

Exercise 1

Don't use a calculator for this exercise.

1 Complete the following additions.

a)
$$\begin{array}{r} 3\ 3 \\ +\ 2\ 2 \\ \hline \end{array}$$

b)
$$\begin{array}{r} 1\ 1 \\ +\ 6\ 9 \\ \hline \end{array}$$

c)
$$\begin{array}{r} 3\ 8 \\ +\ 2\ 7 \\ \hline \end{array}$$

d)
$$\begin{array}{r} 4\ 5 \\ +\ 8\ 3 \\ \hline \end{array}$$

e)
$$\begin{array}{r} 7\ 4 \\ +\ 5\ 5 \\ \hline \end{array}$$

f)
$$\begin{array}{r} 9\ 7 \\ +\ 5\ 8 \\ \hline \end{array}$$

g)
$$\begin{array}{r} 2\ 1\ 1 \\ +\ \ \ 4\ 7 \\ \hline \end{array}$$

h)
$$\begin{array}{r} 8\ 9\ 3 \\ +\ \ \ 2\ 8 \\ \hline \end{array}$$

i)
$$\begin{array}{r} 4\ 7\ 6 \\ +\ \ \ 8\ 2 \\ \hline \end{array}$$

j)
$$\begin{array}{r} 6\ 6\ 5 \\ +\ \ \ 4\ 4 \\ \hline \end{array}$$

k)
$$\begin{array}{r} 9\ 7\ 2 \\ +\ \ \ 6\ 3 \\ \hline \end{array}$$

l)
$$\begin{array}{r} 7\ 7\ 9 \\ +\ \ \ 8\ 6 \\ \hline \end{array}$$

2 Complete the following additions.

a)
$$\begin{array}{r} 1\ 8\ 3 \\ +\ 4\ 5\ 2 \\ \hline \end{array}$$

b)
$$\begin{array}{r} 5\ 4\ 1 \\ +\ 3\ 6\ 7 \\ \hline \end{array}$$

c)
$$\begin{array}{r} 3\ 6\ 7 \\ +\ 4\ 2\ 7 \\ \hline \end{array}$$

d)
$$\begin{array}{r} 2\ 7\ 8 \\ +\ 1\ 9\ 9 \\ \hline \end{array}$$

e)
$$\begin{array}{r} 6\ 0\ 6 \\ +\ 3\ 8\ 8 \\ \hline \end{array}$$

f)
$$\begin{array}{r} 7\ 1\ 3 \\ +\ 9\ 2\ 5 \\ \hline \end{array}$$

g)
$$\begin{array}{r} 2\ 2\ 8 \\ +\ 8\ 7\ 4 \\ \hline \end{array}$$

h)
$$\begin{array}{r} 7\ 9\ 2 \\ +\ 2\ 1\ 7 \\ \hline \end{array}$$

3 Complete the following additions.

a) 9 0 1 2
  +   1 4 6

b) 6 7 0 2
  +   2 3 7

c) 8 3 5 3
  +   3 0 8

d) 6 7 2 1
  +   4 4 9

e) 7 9 9 2
  +   6 4 1

f) 8 8 4 3
  +   2 5 4

g) 5 0 1 2
  + 4 1 4 6

h) 6 7 0 2
  + 2 2 3 7

i) 8 3 5 3
  + 1 3 0 8

j) 6 7 2 1
  + 5 4 4 9

k) 9 9 5 2
  + 1 6 4 1

l) 8 8 4 3
  + 3 2 5 4

4 Work out the answers to these additions.

a) 12 + 928

b) 821 + 72

c) 726 + 28

d) 88 + 212

e) 662 + 928

f) 905 + 929

g) 739 + 115

h) 812 + 426

i) 2710 + 821

j) 7271 + 829

k) 6652 + 981

l) 8210 + 280

m) 3327 + 6202

n) 8202 + 6021

o) 2599 + 7917

p) 9200 + 2863

5 In the morning, 261 people walk through a park. In the afternoon, 769 more people walk through the same park. How many people walk through the park in total?

6 In one day, a theme park sells 3201 day passes and 152 annual passes.
How many passes does the theme park sell in total?

7 Harriet buys a car for £7231 and spends £1621 servicing it.
How much does she spend on her car in total?

8 Complete the following addition questions.

a) 612 + 127 + 82

b) 712 + 21 + 941

c) 883 + 219 + 211

d) 223 + 271 + 991

e) 818 + 1821 + 993

f) 834 + 348 + 1492

g) 1821 + 211 + 2611

h) 7417 + 1411 + 471

Investigate — Jam + Bun

Each of the letters in the words 'JAM' and 'BUN' stand
for a different digit from 1 to 6 so that...

   J A M
+ B U N
7 7 7

a) Can you work out what each of the letters could stand for?

b) Try making your own addition puzzles and get someone else to try them out.

Subtracting Whole Numbers

Example 2   **Work out 759 − 378.**

1. Write the first number above the second number with the units columns lined up.

```
   7 5 9
 − 3 7 8
```

2. Starting with the units column, take the bottom number away from the top number.   9 − 8 = 1

```
   7 5 9
 − 3 7 8
       1
```

3. The top number in the next column is smaller than the bottom number, so 'borrow ten' from the next column along.
This makes the '5' in the tens column into '15', and changes the '7' in the hundreds column into a '6'.   15 − 7 = 8

```
   6 ⁷1̶5 9
 − 3 7 8
      8 1
```

4. Now do the subtraction in the tens column.

5. Finally do the subtraction in the last column using the '6' as the top number.   6 − 3 = 3

```
   6 ⁷1̶5 9
 − 3 7 8
   3 8 1
```

Exercise 2

Don't use a calculator for this exercise.

1   Complete the following subtractions.

a)
```
   7 5
 − 1 4
```
b)
```
   8 2
 − 5 1
```
c)
```
   8 3
 − 7 2
```
d)
```
   6 4
 − 5 1
```

e)
```
   5 0 2
 −   5 1
```
f)
```
   6 3 1
 −   8 1
```
g)
```
   9 0 8
 −   5 6
```
h)
```
   8 3 9
 −   7 7
```

2   Complete the following subtractions.

a)
```
   9 9 9
 − 8 3 1
```
b)
```
   6 7 9
 − 5 6 7
```
c)
```
   4 8 4
 − 3 2 6
```
d)
```
   6 3 2
 − 5 1 7
```

e)
```
   7 5 1
 − 6 8 1
```
f)
```
   6 9 1
 − 4 7 0
```
g)
```
   6 9 3 2
 −   8 2 1
```
h)
```
   5 7 1 2
 −   6 3 2
```

i)
```
   7 6 5 9
 −   1 6 8
```
j)
```
   4 1 8 8
 −   4 6 7
```
k)
```
   6 9 5 8
 −   6 7 1
```
l)
```
   8 9 4 2
 −   7 5 4
```

3 Work out the answers to these subtractions.

a) 51 – 42   **b)** 31 – 28   **c)** 94 – 38   **d)** 66 – 49

e) 462 – 81   **f)** 539 – 83   **g)** 381 – 73   **h)** 655 – 74

i) 990 – 421   **j)** 639 – 541   **k)** 887 – 692   **l)** 483 – 199

m) 3887 – 650   **n)** 1607 – 531   **o)** 4995 – 886   **p)** 5280 – 666

q) 7291 – 371   **r)** 2917 – 248   **s)** 8323 – 601   **t)** 6318 – 237

4   **a)** Find the difference between 92 and 38.

   b) What is 209 subtracted from 381?

   c) Take 592 away from 1497.

   d) How much less is 621 than 8712?

5   866 people are on a train. At a station, 79 people get off.
   How many people are left on the train?

6   A cinema has 207 seats. 162 seats are reserved.
   How many seats in the cinema are not reserved?

7   A jug contains 2632 ml of water. 881 ml of water is poured out of the jug.
   How much water is left in the jug?

8   In a sale, a car has a discount of £529.
   The original price of the car was £7660.
   What is the price of the car in the sale?

9   Penny is trying to raise £8250 for charity. So far, she has raised £442.
   How much more does Penny need to reach her target?

10 6429 people went to a concert on Friday.
   Only 841 people went to the same concert on Sunday.
   How many more people went to the concert on Friday than on Sunday?

Adding Decimals

Decimal numbers can be split up into columns, just like whole numbers.
The columns after the decimal point are called decimal places.

tenths hundredths

units

thousandths

8 . 2 1 3

To add or subtract decimals you have to line up the decimal places,
just as you would with whole numbers.

Example 3 **Work out 1.281 + 2.23.**

1. First write one number above the other, making
   sure that the decimal points line up.

   $$\begin{array}{r} 1.2\,8\,1 \\ +\ 2.2\,3 \\ \hline \end{array}$$

2. Add up the columns from right to left, just as
   you would when adding whole numbers.

   There isn't a digit in the first column for
   the bottom number — so add in a 0.

   $$\begin{array}{r} 1.2\,8\,1 \\ +\ 2.2\,3\,0 \\ \hline 3.5\,{}_1 1\,1 \end{array}$$

3. Include a decimal point in your answer.
   It must line up with the decimal points in the question.

   3 . 5 1 1

Exercise 3

Don't use a calculator for this exercise.

1 Complete the following additions.

a) $\begin{array}{r} 3.1 \\ +\ 3.6 \\ \hline \end{array}$

b) $\begin{array}{r} 5.6 \\ +\ 4.3 \\ \hline \end{array}$

c) $\begin{array}{r} 3.8 \\ +\ 2.4 \\ \hline \end{array}$

d) $\begin{array}{r} 0.7 \\ +\ 4.8 \\ \hline \end{array}$

e) $\begin{array}{r} 2.8 \\ +\ 4.3 \\ \hline \end{array}$

f) $\begin{array}{r} 5.6\,2 \\ +\ 4.3 \\ \hline \end{array}$

g) $\begin{array}{r} 4.3\,4 \\ +\ 6.6 \\ \hline \end{array}$

h) $\begin{array}{r} 4.5\,7 \\ +\ 7.6 \\ \hline \end{array}$

i) $\begin{array}{r} 8.5\,9 \\ +\ 0.6 \\ \hline \end{array}$

j) $\begin{array}{r} 9.0\,8 \\ +\ 3.9 \\ \hline \end{array}$

2 Complete the following additions.

a) $\begin{array}{r} 7.3\,5 \\ +\ 4.2\,2 \\ \hline \end{array}$

b) $\begin{array}{r} 5.6\,4 \\ +\ 2.9\,2 \\ \hline \end{array}$

c) $\begin{array}{r} 6.2\,8 \\ +\ 7.9\,6 \\ \hline \end{array}$

d) $\begin{array}{r} 0.7\,8 \\ +\ 0.5\,4 \\ \hline \end{array}$

e) $\begin{array}{r} 7.6\,3\,4 \\ +\ 5.7\,6 \\ \hline \end{array}$

f) $\begin{array}{r} 9.7\,0\,9 \\ +\ 3.9\,5 \\ \hline \end{array}$

g) $\begin{array}{r} 6.3\,4\,6 \\ +\ 0.7\,4 \\ \hline \end{array}$

h) $\begin{array}{r} 5.0\,9\,6 \\ +\ 7.3\,8 \\ \hline \end{array}$

3 Work out the following additions.

    a)   8.5 3 5   **b)**   7.6 5 6   **c)**   4.8 3 9   **d)**   5.5 4 7   **e)**   8.6 9 1
        + 1.4 6 2   + 3.3 2 8   + 6.3 9 5   + 6.4 5 8   + 4.0 2 8

4 Work out the following calculations.

    a) 7.38 + 2.28   **b)** 0.28 + 8.39   **c)** 7.82 + 1.03   **d)** 3.23 + 9.93

    e) 8.23 + 2.09   **f)** 9.38 + 5.69   **g)** 8.85 + 9.58   **h)** 7.45 + 4.57

    i) 5.321 + 9.057   **j)** 8.481 + 2.381   **k)** 3.048 + 4.831   **l)** 3.571 + 4.699

5   **a)** Add together 3.281 and 5.908.

    b) What is the sum of 29.3 and 21.8?

    c) What is the total of 8.39 and 12.83?

6 Peter buys a chocolate bar for £0.82 and a bag of sweets for £1.93.
How much does Peter spend altogether?

7 Jack spends £30.27 on a jumper and £17.80 on a pair of trousers.
How much does Jack spend in total?

8 Antonia runs 10.88 km on Saturday and 18.28 km on Sunday.
In total, how many kilometres does Antonia run at the weekend?

9 Use the menu to work out the price of
the following groups of items.

    a) Fish and chips.

    b) Fish and mushy peas.

    c) Fish, chicken and chips.

    d) Mushy peas, beans and fish.

    e) A fizzy drink, beans and chicken.

    f) Chicken, beans and mushy peas.

Menu	
Fish	£5.92
Chips	£1.20
Mushy peas	£0.99
Beans	£0.39
Chicken	£4.89
Fizzy drinks (each)	£1.58

Subtracting Decimals

Example 4 Work out 12.04 – 8.57.

1. Write the first number above the second.
   Make sure the decimal points are lined up.

   ```
     1 2.0 4
   –    8.5 7
   ```

2. Starting with the right-hand column, take
   the bottom number away from the top number.

   4 is smaller than 7, so you need to borrow ten from the next
   column to the left. This column contains a zero,
   which means there are no tens in this column to borrow.

   Go another column to the left until you find a non-zero value.
   Borrow ten from this column for the column containing a 0.

   ```
        1 10
     1 2.0 4
   –    8.5 7
   ```

3. The column now has a non-zero value.
   You can borrow ten as usual.

   ```
          9
        1 10 14
     1 2.0 4
   –    8.5 7
   ```

4. Continue with the subtraction, just as you would with
   whole numbers. Include the decimal point in your answer.
   It must line up with the decimal points in the question.

   ```
            9
      0 1 10 14
     1 2.0 4
   –    8.5 7
     0 3.4 7
   ```

Exercise 4

Don't use a calculator for this exercise.

1 Work out the answers to these subtractions.

a)   3.9
    – 1.2

b)   9.2
    – 5.1

c)   6.7
    – 0.8

d)   8.3
    – 4.5

e)   5.8
    – 3.9

f)   6.3 4
    – 5.2

g)   7.7 8
    – 5.8

h)   8.2 1
    – 0.7

i)   8.4
    – 0.2 1

j)   5.8
    – 1.5 8

k)   7.9 3
    – 5.3 1

l)   4.5 7
    – 3.9 1

m)   7.8 4
    – 6.0 9

n)   8.2 4
    – 6.8 3

o)   4.0 1
    – 0.7 2

p)   1 7.9 5
    –   5.7 1

q)   3 0.1 8
    –   4.3 9

r)   4 2.0 3
    –   4.7 1

s)   2 5.1 1
    –   4.0 5

t)   1 0.0 6
    –   5.3 7

2 Work out the answers to these subtractions.

a)
```
   7.4 5 2
 - 4.8 7
```

b)
```
   9.6 2 1
 - 7.2 5
```

c)
```
   8.4 3 9
 - 3.2 8
```

d)
```
   6.6 4 7
 - 5.3 9
```

e)
```
   8.4 5
 - 6.2 2 1
```

f)
```
   5.6 9
 - 0.7 6 8
```

g)
```
   8.4 5
 - 6.5 2 1
```

h)
```
   3.9 8
 - 1.9 7 2
```

i)
```
   4.7 8 6
 - 0.5 7 5
```

j)
```
   8.0 1 1
 - 6.9 2 2
```

k)
```
   7.0 2 5
 - 3.8 3 1
```

l)
```
   8.7 8 1
 - 6.9 6 6
```

3 Work out the following subtractions.

a) $1.8 - 0.7$ b) $2.5 - 1.7$ c) $6.1 - 2.8$ d) $8.1 - 6.7$

e) $17.3 - 2.6$ f) $92.8 - 6.2$ g) $72.2 - 8.1$ h) $17.6 - 2.9$

i) $5.92 - 4.87$ j) $1.18 - 0.88$ k) $7.36 - 4.59$ l) $9.67 - 5.88$

m) $87.38 - 3.64$ n) $92.87 - 5.66$ o) $44.62 - 28.57$ p) $57.62 - 18.19$

q) $8.951 - 6.681$ r) $7.393 - 5.279$ s) $7.565 - 4.956$ t) $7.532 - 4.617$

4 a) Take 5.82 away from 12.391.

b) Subtract 8.281 from 9.507.

c) What is the difference between 66.37 and 27.09?

d) How much larger is 21.271 than 15.18?

5 Peter buys a toy which costs £2.89. How much change would Peter get from £5.00?

6 John is travelling from Beanton to Bakesford. In total, his journey is 98.27 km.
In one day, John travels 39.18 km. How far does John have left to travel in kilometres?

7 Laurence has £50.66 in his bank account. He spends £21.48 of this in the greengrocers.
How much will Laurence have left in his bank account?

8 Eliza buys a new dress for £82.20. How much change would Eliza get from £100?

1.3 Multiplication and Division

Multiplying by 10, 100 and 1000

When a number is <u>multiplied</u> by 10, 100, 1000, etc., each digit in the number moves left:

× 10   each digit moves one place to the left.

× 100   each digit moves two places to the left.

× 1000   each digit moves three places to the left.

Example 1

a) Multiply 69 by 10.

1. To multiply by **10**, move each digit **one** place to the **left**.

2. Fill up the empty space with a **zero**.

b) Multiply 74 by 100.

1. To multiply by **100**, move each digit **two** places to the **left**.

2. Fill up the empty spaces with **zeros**.

c) Multiply 38 by 1000.

1. To multiply by **1000**, move each digit **three** places to the **left**.

2. Fill up the empty spaces with **zeros**.

Example 2 **Calculate 700 × 30.**

1. 30 is the same as 3 × 10, so start by working out 700 × 3.

700 × 3 = 2100

2. Then multiply your answer by 10 to find 700 × 30. To do this move the digits one place to the left.

Then fill the empty space with a zero.

Exercise 1

Don't use a calculator for this exercise.

1 Work out:

a) 6 × 10   b) 4 × 10   c) 9 × 10   d) 71 × 10   e) 63 × 10

f) 50 × 10   g) 269 × 10   h) 480 × 10   i) 227 × 10   j) 313 × 10

2 Work out:

a) 5 × 100   b) 9 × 100   c) 1 × 100   d) 3 × 100

e) 31 × 100   f) 88 × 100   g) 45 × 100   h) 16 × 100

i) 780 × 100   j) 289 × 100   k) 621 × 100   l) 886 × 100

3 Work out:

a) 8 × 1000   b) 3 × 1000   c) 7 × 1000   d) 9 × 1000

e) 63 × 1000   f) 90 × 1000   g) 21 × 1000   h) 52 × 1000

i) 341 × 1000   j) 400 × 1000   k) 942 × 1000   l) 186 × 1000

4 Work out:

a) 6 × 100   b) 82 × 10   c) 681 × 10   d) 712 × 100

e) 2 × 10   f) 821 × 1000   g) 71 × 1000   h) 900 × 100

5 Work out:

a) 80 × 20   b) 30 × 60   c) 50 × 70   d) 400 × 30

e) 20 × 200   f) 500 × 60   g) 600 × 400   h) 500 × 500

i) 300 × 200   j) 400 × 200   k) 700 × 6000   l) 400 × 4000

m) 5000 × 400   n) 7000 × 6000   o) 9000 × 2000   p) 8000 × 3000

6 Work out the missing number in the following multiplications.

a) ..... × 100 = 5000   b) 62 × ..... = 620   c) 74 × ..... = 74 000

d) 18 × ..... = 1800   e) ..... × 300 = 15 000   f) 60 × ..... = 36 000

g) ..... × 900 = 18 000   h) ..... × 70 = 28 000   i) 80 × ..... = 7200

Dividing by 10, 100 and 1000

When a number is <u>divided</u> by 10, 100, 1000, etc., each digit in the number moves right:

÷ 10   each digit moves one place to the right.

÷ 100   each digit moves two places to the right.

÷ 1000   each digit moves three places to the right.

Example 3   Divide 2400 by:

a) 10

1. 2400 is the same as 2400.0.

2. To divide by **10**, move the each digit **one** place to the right. Leave the decimal point where it is.

3. Remove any zeros after the decimal point.

b) 100

1. To divide by **100**, move the each digit **two** places to the **right**. Leave the decimal point where it is.

2. Remove any zeros after the decimal point.

c) 1000

1. To divide by **1000**, move the each digit **three** places to the **right**. Leave the decimal point where it is.

2. Remove any zeros after the decimal point.

Exercise 2

Don't use a calculator for this exercise.

1   Work out:

a) 40 ÷ 10   b) 50 ÷ 10   c) 20 ÷ 10   d) 70 ÷ 10   e) 90 ÷ 10

f) 500 ÷ 10   g) 280 ÷ 10   h) 690 ÷ 10   i) 430 ÷ 10   j) 370 ÷ 10

k) 5700 ÷ 10   l) 4000 ÷ 10   m) 4350 ÷ 10   n) 31 800 ÷ 10   o) 83 070 ÷ 10

2 Work out:

 a) 400 ÷ 100   **b)** 500 ÷ 100   **c)** 800 ÷ 100   **d)** 900 ÷ 100

 e) 700 ÷ 100   **f)** 8200 ÷ 100   **g)** 7700 ÷ 100   **h)** 1000 ÷ 100

 i) 6700 ÷ 100   **j)** 3900 ÷ 100   **k)** 57 000 ÷ 100   **l)** 46 500 ÷ 100

3 Work out:

 a) 9000 ÷ 1000   **b)** 3000 ÷ 1000   **c)** 5000 ÷ 1000   **d)** 7000 ÷ 1000

 e) 16 000 ÷ 1000   **f)** 82 000 ÷ 1000   **g)** 10 000 ÷ 1000   **h)** 55 000 ÷ 1000

 i) 657 000 ÷ 1000   **j)** 490 000 ÷ 1000   **k)** 200 000 ÷ 1000   **l)** 312 000 ÷ 1000

4 Work out:

 a) 45 ÷ 10   **b)** 52 ÷ 10   **c)** 28 ÷ 10   **d)** 715 ÷ 10

 e) 523 ÷ 10   **f)** 309 ÷ 10   **g)** 8182 ÷ 10   **h)** 4344 ÷ 10

 i) 490 ÷ 100   **j)** 580 ÷ 100   **k)** 230 ÷ 100   **l)** 870 ÷ 100

 m) 5720 ÷ 100   **n)** 4320 ÷ 100   **o)** 95 310 ÷ 100   **p)** 76 170 ÷ 100

 q) 4300 ÷ 1000   **r)** 5900 ÷ 1000   **s)** 23 100 ÷ 1000   **t)** 79 600 ÷ 1000

 u) 59 800 ÷ 1000   **v)** 276 400 ÷ 1000   **w)** 248 700 ÷ 1000   **x)** 404 500 ÷ 1000

5 Complete the following divisions.

 a) 42 ÷ 100   **b)** 58 ÷ 100   **c)** 273 ÷ 100   **d)** 734 ÷ 100

 e) 5331 ÷ 100   **f)** 2892 ÷ 100   **g)** 7430 ÷ 1000   **h)** 1090 ÷ 1000

 i) 40 320 ÷ 1000   **j)** 87 250 ÷ 1000   **k)** 254 980 ÷ 1000   **l)** 742 210 ÷ 1000

6 Carla has 6750 g of sweets. She divides the sweets into 10 equal piles.
How many grams of sweets are in each pile?

7 Gloria has 57 litres of lemonade.
She shares the lemonade out into 100 glasses.
How many litres of lemonade are in each glass?

Written Multiplication

Example 4 **Calculate 314 × 23 using the grid method.**

1. Split the numbers up
   into columns and write
   them around a grid.

	300	10	4
20			
3			

2. Multiply each
   separate part
   together in the grid.

	300	10	4
20	300 × 20 = 6000	10 × 20 = 200	4 × 20 = 80
3	300 × 3 = 900	3 × 10 = 30	4 × 3 = 12

3. Add together the
   numbers in the grid.

```
    6 0 0 0
      9 0 0
      2 0 0
        3 0
        8 0
+       1 2
    7 2 2 2
     1 1
```

Example 5 **Calculate 398 × 53 using the column method.**

1. Write one number above the other
   and make sure the columns line up.
   It's best to put the bigger number on the top.

```
    3 9 8
×     5 3
```

2. Start by working out 398 × 3.
   Multiply each digit in 398 by 3, working from right to left.
   If the answer is 10 or more, carry the tens digit.
   E.g. 3 × 8 = 24, so write the 4 in the units column and
   carry the 2. Then 3 × 9 = 27, plus the carried 2 gives 29.

```
    3 9 8
×     5 3
  1 1 9 4
   2 2
```

3. Work out 398 × 50 on the next row.
   You can do this by putting a 0 in the right-hand column
   and multiplying each digit in 398 by 5.
   Work from right to left.

```
      3 9 8
×       5 3
    1 1 9 4
     2 2
  1 9 9 0 0
   4 4
```

4. Add the two rows together to get your final answer.

```
        3 9 8
×         5 3
      1 1 9 4
       2 2
+   1 9 9 0 0
     4 4
    2 1 0 9 4
     1 1
```

Exercise 3

Don't use a calculator for this exercise.

1 Copy and complete the grid to work out 72 × 8.

	70	2
8	70 × 8 = ...	2 × 8 = ...

2 Copy and complete the grid to work out 826 × 9.

	800	20	6
9	800 × ..... = ...	..... × 9 = ...	6 × ..... = ...

3 Copy and complete the grid to work out 731 × 38.

	700	30	1
30	700 × ..... = ...	..... × 30 = ...	1 × ..... = ...
8	..... × ..... = ...	..... × ..... = ...	..... × ..... = ...

4 Use the grid method to work out the following multiplications:

    a) 56 × 5   **b)** 47 × 8   **c)** 6 × 59   **d)** 14 × 32   **e)** 91 × 53

    f) 72 × 45   **g)** 27 × 389   **h)** 391 × 92   **i)** 192 × 11   **j)** 802 × 48

5 Work out the answers to the following multiplications.

    a) 26 × 8   **b)** 83 × 5   **c)** 7 × 65   **d)** 92 × 6   **e)** 4 × 34

    f) 57 × 3   **g)** 9 × 68   **h)** 23 × 8   **i)** 7 × 88   **j)** 5 × 56

6 Work out the answers to the following multiplications.

    a) 84 × 33   **b)** 24 × 23   **c)** 43 × 64   **d)** 17 × 32   **e)** 83 × 27

    f) 32 × 87   **g)** 49 × 76   **h)** 72 × 86   **i)** 23 × 99   **j)** 31 × 55

7 Work out the answers to the following multiplications.

    a) 46 × 427   **b)** 233 × 41   **c)** 58 × 943   **d)** 371 × 93   **e)** 893 × 23

    f) 853 × 38   **g)** 99 × 192   **h)** 237 × 14   **i)** 103 × 92   **j)** 281 × 79

8   Work out the answers to the following multiplications.

a) 3216 × 31   **b)** 5108 × 93   **c)** 6544 × 48   **d)** 7913 × 81

e) 67 × 4810   **f)** 8726 × 17   **g)** 72 × 4651   **h)** 95 × 6843

i) 9028 × 51   **j)** 6506 × 92   **k)** 4820 × 82   **l)** 8269 × 48

m) 5995 × 88   **n)** 59 × 7878   **o)** 4862 × 19   **p)** 29 × 8080

9   Chaz has 8 bags of sweets. Each bag contains 76 sweets.
Use the grid method to work out how many sweets Chaz has in total.

10   A concert hall has 98 rows of seats. There are 32 seats in each row.
Use the column method to work out how many seats there are in the concert hall in total.

11   Dave is ordering food for a party. He works out that the food will cost him £26 per person.
Work out how much will Dave spend if he has a party for:

a) 9 people   **b)** 6 people   **c)** 12 people   **d)** 21 people

e) 63 people   **f)** 44 people   **g)** 33 people   **h)** 82 people

12   Alex has 89 bags of flour, each weighing 12 kg.
How many kilograms of flour does Alex have in total?

13   A hotel charges £129 for a double room for one night.
Work out how much it would cost to stay in the room for 14 nights.

14   A bakery sells 176 loaves of bread a day.
Work out how many loaves of bread the bakery would sell in:

a) 5 days   **b)** 8 days   **c)** 9 days   **d)** 4 days

e) 14 days   **f)** 32 days   **g)** 27 days   **h)** 62 days

15   A shop sells televisions for £548 each.
In one day, it sells 69 televisions.
Work out how much money was spent on televisions in the shop that day.

16 There are 52 playing cards in a pack.
Work out how many cards there will be in:

a) 19 packs   b) 37 packs   c) 49 packs   d) 88 packs

e) 131 packs   f) 804 packs   g) 382 packs   h) 290 packs

17 A car costs £8999.
Work out how much 4 of these cars would cost.

18 Keira earns £1829 in a month.
Given that she earns the same amount each month,
how much will Keira earn in one year?

19 A train travels 1821 kilometres every day.
How many kilometres does the train travel in 84 days?

20 A jug contains 2375 ml of water. Work out how much water would be in:

a) 2 jugs   b) 7 jugs   c) 5 jugs   d) 6 jugs

e) 13 jugs   f) 44 jugs   g) 72 jugs   h) 53 jugs

21 A factory can make 4732 toys a day.
How many toys would the factory be able to make in 47 days?

Investigate — Chinese Multiplication

This Chinese multiplication grid shows that
394 × 84 = **33 096**.

a) Can you figure out how the grid works?
Write a method on how to use the grid.

b) Try the Chinese grid method on some of the
questions in the previous exercise.

c) Do you know any other methods of multiplying numbers?

Written Division

Calculate 443 ÷ 6.

1. Set the division out with the number you're dividing inside a 'box', and the number you're dividing it by outside the box.

$$6\overline{)4\ 4\ 3}$$

2. Start by working out how many times 6 will go into 4.
The answer is 0 as 6 is bigger than 4.
So write a 0 above the box, over the first 4.

$$\begin{array}{r} 0 \\ 6\overline{)4\ 4\ 3} \end{array}$$

3. Since 6 didn't go into 4, now look at the first **two** numbers in the box.
Work out how many times 6 goes into 44.
6 goes into 44 seven times with a remainder of 2.

$6 \times 7 = 42$
$44 - 42 = 2$

So write a 7 above the box (over the second 4), and carry the 2 over to the next column.

$$\begin{array}{r} 0\ 7 \\ 6\overline{)4\ 4\ ^23} \end{array}$$

4. Now look at the last number, with the 2 carried over.

Work out how many times 6 goes into 23.
6 goes into 23 three times with a remainder of 5.

$6 \times 3 = 18$
$24 - 18 = 5$

So write a 3 above the box, over the last column, and write the final remainder.

$$\begin{array}{r} 0\ 7\ 3\ \text{r}\ 5 \\ 6\overline{)4\ 4\ ^23} \end{array}$$

5. Your answer is the number on top of the box, plus the remainder from the last part of the division. $443 \div 6 = $ **73 remainder 5**

Exercise 4

Don't use a calculator for this exercise.

1 Work out the answers to these divisions.

a) $6\overline{)8\ 4}$ b) $4\overline{)9\ 2}$ c) $5\overline{)7\ 5}$ d) $7\overline{)9\ 1}$ e) $3\overline{)7\ 8}$

f) $2\overline{)9\ 6}$ g) $6\overline{)5\ 4}$ h) $7\overline{)8\ 4}$ i) $3\overline{)8\ 7}$ j) $5\overline{)9\ 0}$

2 Work out these divisions. Give your answers as whole numbers with remainders.

a) $4\overline{)9\ 7}$ b) $3\overline{)5\ 9}$ c) $6\overline{)9\ 3}$ d) $2\overline{)8\ 7}$ e) $9\overline{)5\ 5}$

f) $7\overline{)9\ 3}$ g) $4\overline{)9\ 1}$ h) $5\overline{)6\ 9}$ i) $8\overline{)9\ 9}$ j) $4\overline{)8\ 6}$

k) $7\overline{)9\ 5}$ l) $3\overline{)8\ 9}$ m) $6\overline{)8\ 1}$ n) $7\overline{)8\ 8}$ o) $2\overline{)4\ 5}$

Example 7 Calculate 7632 ÷ 36.

1. Start by working out how many times 36 goes into 7.
   The answer is 0 as 36 is bigger than 7.
   So write a 0 above the box, over the 7.

$$\begin{array}{r} 0 \\ 36\overline{)7\ 6\ 3\ 2} \end{array}$$

2. Since 36 didn't go into 7, now look
   at the first two numbers in the box.

   Work out how many times 36 goes into 76.
   36 goes into 76 twice with a remainder of 4.

   So write a 2 above the box, over the 7,
   and carry the 4 over to the next column.

   $36 \times 2 = 72$
   $76 - 72 = 4$

$$\begin{array}{r} 0\ 2 \\ 36\overline{)7\ 6\ {}^4\!3\ 2} \end{array}$$

3. Now look at the next column, with the 4 carried over.

   Work out how many times 36 goes into 43.
   36 goes into 43 once with a remainder of 7.

   So write a 1 above the box, over the 3,
   and carry the 7 over to the next column.

   $36 \times 1 = 36$
   $43 - 36 = 7$

$$\begin{array}{r} 0\ 2\ 1 \\ 36\overline{)7\ 6\ {}^4\!3\ {}^7\!2} \end{array}$$

4. Now look at the last column, with the 7 carried over.

   Work out how many times 36 goes into 72.
   36 goes into 72 twice with no remainder.

   So write a 2 above the box.
   Your answer is the number above the box.

   $36 \times 2 = 72$

$$\begin{array}{r} 0\ \mathbf{2}\ \mathbf{1}\ \mathbf{2} \\ 36\overline{)7\ 6\ {}^4\!3\ {}^7\!2} \end{array}$$

3   Work out the answers to these divisions.

a) $8\overline{)7\ 6\ 8}$ b) $4\overline{)2\ 5\ 2}$ c) $3\overline{)3\ 4\ 2}$ d) $4\overline{)9\ 2\ 4}$

e) $5\overline{)4\ 4\ 5}$ f) $7\overline{)3\ 5\ 7}$ g) $18\overline{)5\ 7\ 6}$ h) $22\overline{)7\ 0\ 4}$

i) $15\overline{)9\ 1\ 5}$ j) $18\overline{)4\ 3\ 2}$ k) $41\overline{)8\ 6\ 1}$ l) $38\overline{)4\ 5\ 6}$

4   Work out these divisions. Give your answers as whole numbers with remainders.

a) $5\overline{)2\ 7\ 4}$ b) $6\overline{)9\ 3\ 1}$ c) $4\overline{)7\ 2\ 3}$ d) $8\overline{)3\ 2\ 9}$

e) $7\overline{)9\ 2\ 2}$ f) $9\overline{)4\ 3\ 8}$ g) $13\overline{)5\ 2\ 5}$ h) $21\overline{)2\ 7\ 7}$

i) $14\overline{)8\ 8\ 3}$ j) $41\overline{)9\ 1\ 4}$ k) $25\overline{)5\ 7\ 7}$ l) $16\overline{)7\ 3\ 9}$

5 Work out the answers to these divisions.

a) $6\overline{)1518}$ b) $7\overline{)4557}$ c) $3\overline{)4638}$ d) $5\overline{)4755}$

e) $9\overline{)9927}$ f) $8\overline{)5808}$ g) $14\overline{)4494}$ h) $21\overline{)4641}$

i) $33\overline{)6996}$ j) $13\overline{)5473}$ k) $12\overline{)6492}$ l) $19\overline{)8018}$

6 Work out these divisions. Give your answers as whole numbers with remainders.

a) $7\overline{)1070}$ b) $4\overline{)7577}$ c) $5\overline{)4063}$ d) $8\overline{)7421}$

e) $13\overline{)8501}$ f) $18\overline{)4173}$ g) $11\overline{)5319}$ h) $13\overline{)8022}$

7 Work out the answers to these divisions.

a) 48 ÷ 3   b) 98 ÷ 7   c) 68 ÷ 2   d) 762 ÷ 6   e) 369 ÷ 9

f) 496 ÷ 8   g) 336 ÷ 14   h) 704 ÷ 22   i) 816 ÷ 16   j) 1232 ÷ 8

k) 4248 ÷ 9   l) 4445 ÷ 7   m) 7088 ÷ 16   n) 4494 ÷ 14   o) 7236 ÷ 18

8 Work out these divisions. Give your answers as whole numbers with remainders.

a) 65 ÷ 7   b) 47 ÷ 3   c) 74 ÷ 5   d) 156 ÷ 8   e) 267 ÷ 4

f) 355 ÷ 6   g) 567 ÷ 11   h) 578 ÷ 15   i) 839 ÷ 13   j) 2211 ÷ 9

k) 3931 ÷ 7   l) 4709 ÷ 5   m) 1880 ÷ 12   n) 3980 ÷ 17   o) 2886 ÷ 14

9 a) Divide 8652 by 14.

b) How many fifteens are there in 3135?

10 A weekend break for four costs £624. How much does it cost per person?

11 Peter shares 782 apples equally into 17 bags. How many apples are in each bag?

12 Bricks are being loaded onto 18 palettes so that
each palette is holding the same number of bricks.
If there are 4223 bricks in total, how many will be left over?

1.4 Calculations with Negative Numbers

Negative Numbers on a Number Line

<u>Negative</u> numbers are numbers that are less than zero.
They're written with a minus sign in front of them.

You can use a <u>number line</u> to help with calculations involving negative numbers.

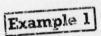 **Use the number line to work out:**

a) −4 + 7

1. Start at −4.
2. Count 7 places up (right).
3. You finish at 3, so: −4 + 7 = **3**

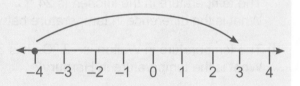

b) 2 − 8

1. Start at 2.
2. Count 8 places down (left).
3. You finish at −6, so: 2 − 8 = **−6**

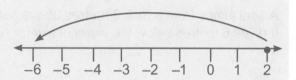

Exercise 1

Don't use a calculator for this exercise.

1   Work out the following, using a number line if you need to.

a) −6 + 8   b) −5 + 9   c) −7 + 4   d) −12 + 15

e) −16 + 8   f) −5 + 17   g) −2 + 19   h) −11 + 9

i) −12 + 15   j) −2 + 18   k) −16 + 20   l) −15 + 6

m) −13 + 11   n) −25 + 7   o) −12 + 21   p) −18 + 19

2   Work out:

a) 3 − 9   b) 6 − 10   c) 4 − 15   d) 8 − 12

e) 11 − 16   f) 8 − 15   g) 9 − 34   h) 12 − 26

i) 11 − 19   j) 7 − 15   k) 20 − 26   l) 10 − 19

m) 14 − 22   n) 8 − 19   o) 12 − 18   p) 21 − 30

3 Work out:

a) −8 − 4

b) −3 − 11

c) −6 − 4

d) −12 − 7

e) −2 − 16

f) −12 − 15

g) −21 − 10

h) −25 − 18

i) −6 − 23

j) −15 − 21

k) −32 − 12

l) −31 − 22

4 a) What is the difference in temperature between −7 °C and 19 °C?

b) What is the difference in temperature between 35 °C and −4 °C?

c) The temperature inside a freezer is −18 °C.
The temperature in the kitchen is 24 °C.
What is the difference in temperature between the freezer and the kitchen?

d) The temperature in Walton is −2 °C. It is 31 °C warmer in Harpury.
What is the temperature in Harpury?

5 A seal jumps from a rock 3 metres above sea level, into the sea.
It dives 6 metres below the water. How far has the seal dived in total?

6 Clive goes shopping with £86 in his bank account.
He leaves the first shop and is £13 overdrawn,
i.e. he has spent £13 more than he originally had in his account.

a) How much did Clive spend in the first shop?

b) Clive goes into a second shop and spends a further £33.
By how much is Clive overdrawn now?

Investigate — Multiplying Negatives

Use a calculator to do the following multiplications:

a) A positive number × a negative number.

b) A negative number × a positive number.

c) A negative number × a negative number.

d) A negative number × a negative number × a negative number.

Do you get a positive or a negative answer for each one?
See if you can write some rules for the outcomes of a)-d).
Test them out with some different numbers.

1.5 Calculators, BODMAS and Checking

BODMAS

Operations in a calculation are things like addition, subtraction, multiplication and division.

The order you do these things in is really important.

BODMAS tells you the order you should do things in a calculation:

BRACKETS ←——————— Work out things in **brackets** first.

OTHER ←——————— Then do other things like **squaring** and **powers**.

DIVISION
MULTIPLICATION ←——————— **Divide/Multiply** groups of numbers working from left to right.

ADDITION
SUBTRACTION ←——————— **Add/Subtract** groups of numbers working from left to right.

Example 1 Work out $12 - 3 \times 3 + 8$.

1. This calculation involves subtraction, multiplication and addition.

2. BODMAS tells us that the **multiplication** needs to be done first.

    $3 \times 3 = 9$

    $12 - 9 + 8$

3. Working from left to right, the **subtraction** needs to be done next.

    $12 - 9 = 3$

4. Finally, do the **addition**.

    $3 + 8 = 11$

Example 2 Work out $7 \times (10 - 4) + 11$.

1. This calculation involves multiplication, brackets, subtraction and addition.

2. BODMAS tells us that the things inside the **brackets** need to be done first.

    $(10 - 4) = 6$

    $7 \times 6 + 11$

3. The two operations left are multiplication and addition. The **multiplication** needs to be done next.

    $7 \times 6 = 42$

4. Finally, do the **addition**.

    $42 + 11 = 53$

Exercise 1

Don't use a calculator for this exercise.

1 For each calculation, list the operations in the order they should be done.
   You do not need to work out the answers.

   a) $8 + 3 \times 11$ **b)** $25 \div 5 - 2$ **c)** $24 - 3 \times 4$ **d)** $18 - 6 \div 6$

   e) $18 - 48 \div 8 + 3$ **f)** $10 \times 2 - 22 \div 2$ **g)** $11 \times 8 + 2 - 14$ **h)** $66 \div 6 + 2 \times 9$

2 Use BODMAS to answer these questions.

   a) $4 + 1 \times 5$ **b)** $6 \div 3 + 9$ **c)** $11 \times 3 + 5$ **d)** $12 \div 6 + 15$

   e) $12 + 12 \div 6$ **f)** $10 \times 8 - 7$ **g)** $12 \times 4 + 18$ **h)** $72 \div 8 + 22$

   i) $90 - 7 \times 12$ **j)** $12 + 30 \div 6$ **k)** $55 \div 11 \times 4$ **l)** $12 + 81 \div 9$

3 Use BODMAS to answer these questions.

   a) $6 \times (5 - 2)$ **b)** $48 \div (10 - 6)$ **c)** $11 \times (22 \div 2)$

   d) $(22 - 15) \times 8$ **e)** $(12 - 6) \times 7$ **f)** $144 \div (4 \times 3)$

   g) $(29 + 7) \div 3$ **h)** $(5 + 6) \times 2$ **i)** $10 \times (22 - 12)$

   j) $(5 + 6) \times 3$ **k)** $5 \times (36 \div 4)$ **l)** $(50 - 41) \times 7$

   m) $44 \div (2 + 2)$ **n)** $(60 - 28) \div 4$ **o)** $77 \div (30 - 23)$

4 Use BODMAS to answer these questions.

   a) $8 \times (12 - 5)$ **b)** $(9 + 10) \times 2$ **c)** $108 \div 12 + 20$ **d)** $96 \div 8 - 2$

   e) $(18 + 22) \div 10$ **f)** $50 - 4 \times 4$ **g)** $5 \times (8 + 7)$ **h)** $(6 + 6) \times 4$

   i) $7 \times (14 - 2)$ **j)** $42 \div (2 + 4)$ **k)** $2 \times (69 \div 3)$ **l)** $11 \times (18 - 6)$

5 Use BODMAS to answer these questions.

   a) $5 \times 5 - 16 \div 2$ **b)** $9 + 10 \times 2 \div 4$ **c)** $22 - 3 \times 2 + 8$ **d)** $6 \times 8 - 15 \div 3$

   e) $9 \div 3 + 2 \times 9$ **f)** $31 + 4 - 6 \times 4$ **g)** $36 - 2 + 32 \div 8$ **h)** $9 \times 7 + 11 - 8$

   i) $19 + 6 \times 3 - 4$ **j)** $10 + 16 \div 8 \times 5$ **k)** $60 - 6 \times 9 - 1$ **l)** $80 \div 4 - 2 \times 6$

6 Use BODMAS to answer these questions.

a) 12 × (12 − 9) ÷ 9

b) (16 − 3) + 8 ÷ 2

c) 36 ÷ 3 × (11 − 5)

d) (3 + 32) + 6 × 4

e) (4 + 6) × 4 + 32

f) 9 × (16 − 6) ÷ 3

g) 8 × 9 − (12 + 24)

h) 5 × (9 + 3) − 11

i) (22 + 22) − 63 ÷ 9

Investigate — Four 4s Make...

Can you make every whole number from 0 upwards by
putting the symbols +, −, ×, ÷ or brackets between the numbers 4, 4, 4 and 4?

E.g. 4 ÷ 4 = **1**,   4 ÷ 4 + 4 ÷ 4 = **2**   etc.

You don't have to use all four numbers each time.
Remember to use what you know about the order of operations from BODMAS.

Using Calculators

When doing calculations with lots of operations,
you'll need to use these buttons on your calculator:

open brackets ——— ( ) ——— close brackets

multiplication ——— X ÷ ——— division

addition ——— + − ——— subtraction

= ——— equals

You can tell the calculator what order to do the operations in by putting <u>brackets</u>
into the calculation. Calculators will work out the things in brackets first.

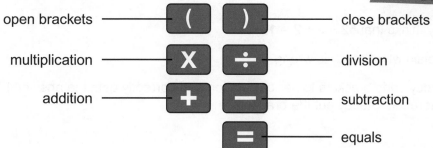

Example 3 **Add brackets to the following calculation so it is correct when worked out on a calculator: 18 − 3 × 5 = 75**

1. There are two possible places
   for the brackets to go.

   18 − (3 × 5) or (18 − 3) × 5

2. Enter each option in on your calculator to see
   which gives you the right answer.

   18 − (3 × 5) = 3

   (18 − 3) × 5 = 75

Exercise 2

1 There are two places to put a pair of brackets in the following calculations. For each one, write out the calculation with the brackets in each position, and work out the answer.

a) $10 \div 2 + 3$ b) $3 \times 7 - 4$ c) $3 \times 4 + 6$ d) $12 \div 3 \times 2$

e) $60 + 12 \div 6$ f) $24 + 12 \div 6$ g) $10 \times 2 + 11$ h) $25 - 8 \times 3$

i) $7 + 2 \times 9$ j) $40 - 36 \div 4$ k) $84 \div 7 + 5$ l) $27 - 9 \div 9$

2 Add brackets to these calculations so they're correct.
Check your answers on a calculator.

a) $16 \div 8 \times 2 = 1$ b) $60 \div 5 + 5 = 6$ c) $8 - 6 \times 12 = 24$

d) $14 - 2 \times 6 = 72$ e) $6 + 3 \times 4 = 36$ f) $4 + 2 \times 7 = 42$

g) $88 + 55 \div 11 = 13$ h) $60 + 10 \div 7 = 10$ i) $42 + 3 \div 9 = 5$

j) $8 - 1 \times 9 = 63$ k) $36 \div 3 + 3 = 6$ l) $22 - 7 \times 2 = 30$

m) $4 \times 10 + 2 = 48$ n) $150 - 6 \div 12 = 12$ o) $50 - 2 \div 6 = 8$

3 Stacey thinks that $52 \div 2 + 2 = 13$.

a) Explain why Stacey is wrong.

b) Stacey adds brackets to her calculation and correctly gets the answer 13.
Where has Stacey put the brackets?

4 Add one pair of brackets to each of these calculations so they're correct.
Use your calculator to check each one.

a) $3 + 5 \times 6 - 2 = 23$ b) $8 - 2 \times 4 + 8 = 32$

c) $40 \div 8 \div 2 \times 11 = 110$ d) $9 + 1 - 10 - 2 = 2$

e) $9 \times 6 + 3 - 7 = 74$ f) $99 \div 12 - 3 + 11 = 22$

g) $15 - 12 \times 3 \times 12 = 108$ h) $18 - 9 + 5 \times 11 = 44$

5 Paul thinks that $3 \times 10 + 9 \div 3 = 19$.

a) Explain why Paul is wrong.

b) Add brackets to the calculation to make Paul's answer correct on a calculator.

Checking Answers

One way to check your answers is to do the opposite calculation.

Addition and **subtraction** are opposites.

If you start off with a number, add any number to it and then subtract the same number from the answer, you'll end up with your original number.

Multiplying and **dividing** are opposites.

If you start off with a number, multiply it by any number and then divide the answer by the same number, you'll end up with your original number.

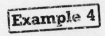 **Example 4** **What calculation could you do to check that $10 \div 2 = 5$?**

1. First identify what sort of calculation the question is. This is a **division**.

   $10 \oplus 2 = 5$

2. **Multiplication** is the opposite of **division**. If you multiply your answer by the number you divided by, you should get the number you started with.

   $5 \times 2 = 10$

   (You could also check that $10 \div 5 = 2$.)

Exercise 3

1 Write a calculation you could use to check the following.

a) $19 + 8 = 27$ b) $6 + 11 = 17$ c) $21 - 14 = 7$ d) $42 - 22 = 20$

e) $15 - 9 = 6$ f) $7 + 18 = 25$ g) $24 - 15 = 9$ h) $16 + 11 = 27$

i) $22 - 17 = 5$ j) $15 + 19 = 34$ k) $39 - 22 = 17$ l) $25 + 12 = 37$

m) $31 - 10 = 21$ n) $22 - 4 = 18$ o) $28 + 14 = 42$ p) $10 + 29 = 39$

2 Write an opposite calculation for each of the following.

a) $5 \times 5 = 25$ b) $4 \times 3 = 12$ c) $42 \div 6 = 7$ d) $72 \div 8 = 9$

e) $8 \times 4 = 32$ f) $7 \times 3 = 21$ g) $5 \times 10 = 50$ h) $18 \div 9 = 2$

i) $90 \div 10 = 9$ j) $12 \div 6 = 2$ k) $121 \div 11 = 11$ l) $96 \div 8 = 12$

m) $63 \div 9 = 7$ n) $8 \times 8 = 64$ o) $7 \times 11 = 77$ p) $11 \times 12 = 132$

Section 2 — Approximations

2.1 Rounding

Whole Numbers

Numbers are sometimes approximated (or rounded) to make them easier to work with.

For example, the number 3274 could be rounded:

> • to the nearest ten (3270)
> • to the nearest hundred (3300)
> • to the nearest thousand (3000)

Example 1

a) **Round 46 to the nearest ten.**

Look at the digit in the units column.
It's more than 5, so round up.

46 — round up to **50**

b) **Round 210 to the nearest hundred.**

Look at the digit in the tens column.
It's less than 5, so round down.

210 — round down to **200**

c) **Round 3525 to the nearest thousand.**

Look at the digit in the hundreds column.
It's equal to 5, so round up.

3525 — round up to **4000**

Exercise 1

1 Round each of these numbers to the nearest 10.

a) 32   b) 74   c) 26   d) 13

e) 48   f) 7   g) 55   h) 63

i) 118   j) 324   k) 401   l) 589

2 Round each of these numbers to the nearest 100.

a) 280   b) 420   c) 315   d) 685

e) 542   f) 871   g) 352   h) 749

i) 1230   j) 2350   k) 4567   l) 5257

3   Round each of these numbers to the nearest 1000.

    a) 1300   **b)** 6500   **c)** 4900   **d)** 2770   **e)** 1450

    f) 5320   **g)** 7190   **h)** 4589   **i)** 2458   **j)** 976

4   Round each of these numbers to the nearest 1000.

    a) 12 400   **b)** 15 700   **c)** 27 500   **d)** 33 450   **e)** 99 120

    f) 59 890   **g)** 17 984   **h)** 38 385   **i)** 47 158   **j)** 50 653

5   Round 5265 to the nearest:

    a) ten   **b)** hundred   **c)** thousand

6   Round 7854 to the nearest:

    a) ten   **b)** hundred   **c)** thousand

7   There are 14 780 supporters at a football match. Round this number to the nearest 1000.

8   A whole number rounds to 250 to the nearest ten and 200 to the nearest 100.
    List all the numbers this could be.

9   A whole number rounds to 350 to the nearest ten and 400 to the nearest 100.
    List all the numbers this could be.

10   Round 8999 to the nearest:

    a) ten   **b)** hundred   **c)** thousand

11   What is the smallest possible number that would round to 200
    when rounded to the nearest hundred?

12   The number of people in a town is 23 000 to the nearest 1000.
    What is the greatest number of people there could be in the town?

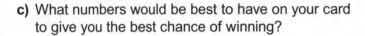

Investigate — Rounding Bingo

a) Play a game of rounding bingo.
- Pick someone to be the 'bingo caller'.
- Write down 6 numbers between 1 and 49 on a card.
- The bingo caller selects numbers at random between 1 and 49.
- If a number on your card is called, cross it off.
- If a number is called which rounds (to the nearest 10) to a number on your card, cross the number off your card — so if 29 was called, you could cross off 30.
- The winner is the first person to cross off all 6 numbers on their card.

b) For each number on your card, write down all the called numbers which would allow you to cross off that number.

c) What numbers would be best to have on your card to give you the best chance of winning?

Decimals

Numbers with <u>decimal places</u> can also be <u>rounded</u>.
They're often rounded to the nearest <u>whole number</u>.

For example, 3.9 would be rounded to 4 to the nearest whole number.

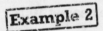

a) Round 5.1 to the nearest whole number.

Look at the digit in the tenths column (the first column after the decimal point). It's less than 5, so round down.

5.1 — round down to **5**

b) Round 12.6 to the nearest whole number.

Look at the digit in the tenths column. It's more than 5, so round up.

12.6 — round up to **13**

c) Round 6.58 to the nearest whole number.

Look at the digit in the tenths column. It's equal to 5, so round up.

6.58 — round up to **7**

Exercise 2

1   Round each of these numbers to the nearest whole number.

    a) 4.3   **b)** 8.7   **c)** 1.8   **d)** 6.5

    e) 2.1   **f)** 7.9   **g)** 11.2   **h)** 18.6

    i) 28.8   **j)** 45.3   **k)** 108.5   **l)** 29.7

2   Choose the numbers from the box which round to 5 to the nearest whole number.

5.2	5.8	4.6	5.3	4.2	5.5	4.9	4.5

3   Round each of these numbers to the nearest whole number.

    a) 6.25   **b)** 8.94   **c)** 2.49   **d)** 6.81

    e) 5.51   **f)** 18.49   **g)** 1.32   **h)** 7.99

    i) 19.42   **j)** 25.34   **k)** 91.28   **l)** 9.68

4   Choose the numbers from the box which round to 12 to the nearest whole number.

12.15	11.65	11.46	12.06	12.53	12.29	11.87	12.58

5   Write down a number between 3 and 4 that has one decimal place and rounds to 3 when rounded to the nearest whole number.

6   Write down a number between 10 and 11 that has two decimal places and rounds to 11 when rounded to the nearest whole number.

7   Write down 5 numbers that round to 15 to the nearest whole number.

8   A slug measures 8 cm to the nearest cm. What is the shortest it can measure?

9   What is the smallest possible number that would round to 1 when rounded to the nearest whole number?

2.2 Estimating

Estimating Answers by Rounding

You can <u>estimate</u> the answer to a calculation by <u>rounding</u> the numbers in the calculation to easier ones — usually by rounding to the nearest 10 or nearest 100.

Even though the answer isn't exactly right, it can still be useful.

Example 1 Use rounding to estimate the answers to:

a) 17 × 28

1. Round both numbers in the calculation to numbers that are easier to use.

   To the nearest 10, 17 rounds to 20 and 28 rounds to 30.

2. Rewrite the calculation using the rounded numbers.

   So estimate 17 × 28 using 20 × 30 = **600**

b) 626 ÷ 13

1. Round both numbers, using the most suitable accuracy for those numbers.

   To the nearest 100, 626 rounds to 600 and to the nearest 10, 13 rounds to 10.

2. Rewrite the calculation using the rounded numbers.

   So estimate 626 ÷ 13 using 600 ÷ 10 = **60**

Example 2 Use rounding to estimate the answer to 48 ÷ 2.1.

1. Round both numbers in the calculation to numbers that are easier to use.

   To the nearest 10, 48 rounds to 50 and to the nearest whole number, 2.1 rounds to 2.

2. Rewrite the calculation using the rounded numbers.

   So estimate 48 ÷ 2.1 using 50 ÷ 2 = **25**

Exercise 1

Don't use a calculator for this exercise.

1 **a)** Round 325 and 185 to the nearest hundred.

   b) Use your answer to part **a)** to estimate 325 + 185.

2 **a)** Round 476 and 206 to the nearest hundred.

   b) Use your answer to part **a)** to estimate 476 − 206.

3 **a)** Round 778 and 483 to the nearest hundred.

   b) Use your answer to part **a)** to estimate 778 − 483.

4 **a)** Round 58 and 9 to the nearest ten.

   b) Use your answer to part **a)** to estimate 58 ÷ 9.

5 **a)** Round 27 and 13 to the nearest ten.

   b) Use your answer to part **a)** to estimate 27 × 13.

6 By rounding to the nearest 10, estimate 451 + 234.

7 By rounding to the nearest 10, estimate 886 − 395.

8 By rounding to the nearest 10, estimate 39 × 12.

9 By rounding to the nearest 10, estimate 104 × 9.

10 By rounding to the nearest 10, estimate 47 ÷ 13.

11 By rounding to the nearest 100, estimate 304 ÷ 99.

12 Use rounding to estimate the answer to each of these calculations.

   a) 614 + 258   **b)** 198 + 176   **c)** 579 − 189

   d) 907 − 294   **e)** 32 × 16   **f)** 82 × 8

   g) 126 × 11   **h)** 88 ÷ 9   **i)** 84 ÷ 22

   j) 384 ÷ 41   **k)** 613 ÷ 104   **l)** 998 ÷ 186

13 After a party, each child is given a party bag. There are 18 sweets in each party bag, and 22 children went to the party. Estimate the total number of sweets given out.

14 a) Round 52 to the nearest 10 and 4.7 to the nearest whole number.

 b) Use your answer to part **a)** to estimate 52 ÷ 4.7.

15 a) Round 317 to the nearest 100 and 6.2 to the nearest whole number.

 b) Use your answer to part **a)** to estimate 317 × 6.2.

16 Use rounding to estimate the answer to each of these calculations.

 a) 78 × 2.3 **b)** 34 × 2.9 **c)** 103 × 3.5

 d) 67 ÷ 7.2 **e)** 89 ÷ 2.7 **f)** 39.6 ÷ 4.9

17 Gemma makes a chain of paperclips. Each paperclip is 4.8 cm long, and she uses 23 paperclips in her chain. Use rounding to estimate the length of the chain.

18 A chocolate bar is 15.3 cm long. John bites 7.2 cm off the end of the chocolate bar. Use rounding to estimate how much of the chocolate bar is left.

19 A train ticket costs £9.80. Use rounding to estimate the cost of 21 train tickets.

20 A pack of 18 hot cross buns costs £2.10.
Use rounding to estimate the cost in pence of one hot cross bun.

> ## Investigate — Human Pyramid
>
> **a)** Design a human pyramid using every member of your class. Count the number of people and make a rough plan of your pyramid.
>
> **b)** What is a typical width and height of a kneeling person? Round these numbers and use them to estimate the height and width of the pyramid.
>
> **c)** How much bigger would the pyramid be if you used everyone in your year? How much bigger would it be if it used everyone in the school?

Section 3 — Powers

3.1 Powers

Squares

Squaring a number means multiplying that number by itself.

For example, the square of 4 is 4 × 4 and is written as 4^2 (you'd say "four squared").

The square of a number is always positive.

You can work out squares on your calculator using the button that looks like this: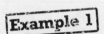

So press 3 x^2 and the calculator works out $3^2 = 3 \times 3 = 9$.

Example 1

Find: a) 3^2 $3^2 = 3 \times 3 = \mathbf{9}$

b) $(-3)^2$ $(-3)^2 = (-3) \times (-3) = \mathbf{9}$

c) **What do you notice about your answers?**   They are **the same**.

Exercise 1

1 Copy and complete these calculations:

   a) 5^2 = ... × ..... = 25

   b) 2^2 = 2 × ..... = ...

   c) 6^2 = ... × ..... = 36

   d) 4^2 = ... = ...

2 Copy and complete this table. Don't use your calculator.

a	1	7	8	9	10
a^2					

3 Work out the following.
   You may use a calculator if you need to.

   a) 12^2 **b)** 15^2 **c)** 11^2

   d) 13^2 **e)** 40^2 **f)** 35^2

   g) 60^2 **h)** 50^2 **i)** 100^2

4 For each of the following:

   i) write the square as a multiplication.

   ii) work out the multiplication, using a calculator if you need to.

   a) $(-2)^2$ **b)** $(-5)^2$ **c)** $(-10)^2$

   d) $(-6)^2$ **e)** $(-13)^2$ **f)** 0.1^2

   g) 0.6^2 **h)** 0.4^2 **i)** 1.5^2

   j) $(-0.1)^2$ **k)** $(-0.5)^2$ **l)** $(-1.4)^2$

Investigate — Number Patterns

Here are the first four shapes in a pattern:

a) How many dots will be in the next shape in the pattern?

b) Draw out the next 5 shapes and count the dots.
   What do you notice about the numbers of dots?

c) Can you work out how many dots will be in the 100th shape?

Cubes

Cubing a number means multiplying that number by itself, then by itself again
(i.e. multiplying 3 lots of that number together).

The cube of 4 is 4 × 4 × 4 and is written as 4^3 (you'd say "four cubed").
The cube of a positive number is <u>positive</u>, but the cube of a negative number is <u>negative</u>.

You can work out cubes on your calculator using the button that looks like this:
So press **4** x^3 and the calculator works out 4^3 = 4 × 4 × 4 = 64.

Example 2

Find: **a) 3^3** 3^3 = 3 × 3 × 3 = **27**

   b) $(-3)^3$ $(-3)^3$ = (−3) × (−3) × (−3) = **−27**

   c) What do you notice about your answers?
            The numbers are the same, but the sign changes.
            (i.e. one is positive and one is negative)

Exercise 2

1 Copy and complete these calculations. Don't use a calculator.

   a) 2^3 = ... × 2 × ..... = ...

   b) 6^3 = ... × ..... × ..... = 216

   c) 5^3 = ... = ...

2 Copy and complete the table to find these cube numbers. Don't use a calculator.

a	1	3	4	8	10
a^3		27			

3 Work out the following.
    You may use a calculator if you need to.

   a) 7^3 **b)** 12^3 **c)** 11^3

   d) 9^3 **e)** 13^3 **f)** 18^3

   g) 20^3 **h)** 15^3 **i)** 30^3

4 For each of the following:

    i) write the cube as a multiplication.

    ii) work out the multiplication, using a calculator if you need to.

a) $(-2)^3$

b) $(-6)^3$

c) $(-12)^3$

d) $(-5)^3$

e) $(-10)^3$

f) 0.5^3

g) 0.4^3

h) 1.6^3

i) $(-0.2)^3$

j) $(-0.1)^3$

k) $(-0.3)^3$

l) $(-4.5)^3$

3.2 Roots

Square Roots

Finding the <u>square root</u> of a number is the opposite of <u>squaring</u> it.

To find square roots on your calculator, use this button:

So press   and the calculator works out $\sqrt{256} = 16$.

Watch out though — a calculator will only give you the <u>positive</u> square root.

There's also a <u>negative</u> answer for every positive one you find.

For example, the square roots of 4 are 2 and –2.

Example 1   **Find both square roots of 36.**

1. You need to find the number that when multiplied by itself gives 36.

2. $36 = 6 \times 6$, so the positive square root is 6. $\sqrt{36} = 6$

3. Don't forget the negative square root. $-\sqrt{36} = -6$

Exercise 1

1 Copy and complete each of the following:

   a) $4 = 2 \times$ ......
     So $\sqrt{4}$ = ... and $-\sqrt{4}$ = ...

   b) $9 = 3 \times$ ......
     So $\sqrt{9}$ = ... and $-\sqrt{9}$ = ...

2 Copy and complete this table without using a calculator.

x	16	25	36	81	100
$\sqrt{x}$	4				
$-\sqrt{x}$	−4				

3 Without using a calculator, find:

   a) $\sqrt{25}$ **b)** $-\sqrt{25}$ **c)** $\sqrt{64}$ **d)** $-\sqrt{64}$

   e) $\sqrt{121}$ **f)** $-\sqrt{121}$ **g)** $\sqrt{144}$ **h)** $-\sqrt{144}$

4 Find both square roots of these numbers. You may use a calculator if you need to.

   a) 256   **b)** 361   **c)** 400   **d)** 10 000

   e) 225   **f)** 625   **g)** 324   **h)** 196

5 Use your calculator to find both square roots of these decimals.

   a) 0.36   **b)** 2.56   **c)** 0.81

   d) 0.25   **e)** 1.69   **f)** 16.81

Investigate — Squaring Square Roots

a) Using a calculator, find $\sqrt{2}$.
Write down all the digits from your calculator screen.

b) What would you expect to get if you squared this number?

c) Type in the digits you've written down use your calculator to square it.
Did you get what you expected? If not, why not?

d) Try it with $\sqrt{2}$, $\sqrt{3}$, $\sqrt{4}$... all the way up to $\sqrt{10}$.
Do you get the same results every time? If not, why not?

Section 4 — Multiples, Factors and Primes

4.1 Multiples

Multiples

The <u>multiples</u> of a number are just the numbers that are in its <u>times table</u>.

So the multiples of 3 are 3, 6, 9, 12, 15, ... and the multiples of 10 are 10, 20, 30, 40, 50, ...

Example 1

a) **List the first five multiples of 6.**

Just write down the first five numbers in the 6 times table:

6, 12, 18, 24, 30

b) **Which of the numbers in the box are:**
(i) multiples of 4?
(ii) multiples of 7?

| 14 | 16 | 2 | 24 | 28 | 8 |

4 divides into 16, 24, 28 and 8 exactly —
so these numbers are multiples of 4.
But 4 doesn't divide into 14 or 2 exactly —
so these aren't multiples of 4.

(i) **16, 24, 28, and 8**

7 divides into 14 and 28 exactly,
but not into 16, 2, 24 or 8.

(ii) **14 and 28**

Exercise 1

1   List the first five multiples of:

    a) 2   **b)** 5   **c)** 7

    d) 9   **e)** 8   **f)** 11

2   Write down the numbers from the box that are:

    a) multiples of 6

    b) multiples of 8

| 36 | 25 | 7 | 15 | 18 | 24 | 16 |
| 19 | 12 | 30 | 32 | 22 | 28 | 40 |

3   Write down all the multiples of 12 that are less than 50.

---

4 Write down all the multiples of 9 between 30 and 60.

5 **a)** Find the only multiple of 11 between 30 and 40.

b) List the multiples of 7 between 20 and 50.

c) Find the only multiple of 8 between 50 and 60.

6 **a)** List all the multiples of 2 between 11 and 25.

b) List all the multiples of 3 between 11 and 25.

c) List all the numbers between 11 and 25 that are multiples of both 2 and 3.

7 Write down all the numbers from the box that **aren't** multiples of 9.

22	27	54	17	18	23	45
9	90	63	65	77	49	36

Lowest Common Multiples

A common multiple is a number that's in the times table of two or more different numbers.

The lowest common multiple (LCM) of a group of numbers is the smallest common multiple of those numbers. It's the lowest number they all divide into ('go into') exactly.

Example 2   Find the lowest common multiple of 3 and 4.

1. Write down the multiples of 3 and 4:

2. Circle all the numbers that appear in both lists — these are the common multiples.

multiples of 3:
3, 6, 9, ⑫ 15, 18, 21, ㉔, ...
multiples of 4:
4, 8, ⑫ 16, 20, ㉔ 28, ...

3. The lowest common multiple is the smallest of the common multiples (the smallest number that's in both lists of multiples).

Common multiples are 12, 24, ...

LCM of 3 and 4 is **12**.

Exercise 2

1 **a)** Write down the first ten multiples of 2.

   b) Write down the first ten multiples of 3.

   c) Write down the common multiples of 2 and 3 from your lists.

   d) Find the lowest common multiple — the smallest number that's in your list from part **c)**.

2 **a)** Write down the first eight multiples of 4.

   b) Write down the first eight multiples of 7.

   c) Find the lowest common multiple of 4 and 7.

3 **a)** Write down the first five multiples of 6.

   b) Write down the first five multiples of 9.

   c) Find the lowest common multiple of 6 and 9.

4 Find the lowest common multiple (LCM) of each of the following pairs of numbers.

   a) 3 and 5   **b)** 2 and 7   **c)** 4 and 5

   d) 5 and 9   **e)** 3 and 7   **f)** 8 and 9

Investigate — Lowest Common Multiples

Emily says, "*the lowest common multiple of two numbers can be found by multiplying the two numbers together*".

   a) Give some examples to show that Emily's rule sometimes works.

   b) Give some examples of numbers to show that her rule doesn't always work.

   c) Try and work out when Emily's rule works and when it doesn't. Can you come up with a rule?

Factors

The <u>factors</u> of a number are all the numbers that divide into it ('go into it') exactly.

So the factors of 6 are 1, 2, 3 and 6 — all these numbers go into 6 exactly.

Example 1   **Find all the factors of 18.**

1. Start by writing 1 × 18.

2. Then try 2 × something to make 18.
   2 × 9 = 18, so write this on the next row.

3. Carry on trying to make 18 by multiplying pairs of numbers: 3 × something, 4 × something etc.

4. Write each pair of numbers in a new row. Put a dash if a number doesn't divide exactly.

5. Stop when you get a repeated number (6).

6. Write down all the numbers in the multiplications.

Increasing by 1 each time ↓

1 × 18
2 × 9
3 × 6
4 × —
5 × —
6 × 3

So the factors of 18 are
1, 2, 3, 6, 9 and 18

Exercise 1

1   Copy and complete the boxes to find all the factors of:

a) 15

```
1 × 15
2 × —
3 × ....
4 × ....
5 × 3
```

b) 24

```
1 × 24
2 × 12
3 × ....
4 × ....
5 × ....
6 × 4
```

2   Write down the numbers from the box that are factors of:

a) 10   b) 13   c) 30

d) 28   e) 22   f) 32

```
2  7  1  4  5  8
```

3 The number 9 has three factors. Find them all.

4 The number 21 has four factors. Find them all.

5 Find all the factors of each of these numbers.

a) 7   b) 25   c) 16

d) 45   e) 64   f) 48

6 Write down the numbers from the box that are factors of both:

a) 8 and 28

| 3 | 5 | 4 | 7 | 2 | 8 |

b) 15 and 21

Investigate — The Factor Game

a) Starting from 100, divide by a number between 2 and 9 to get a whole number. Keep dividing by a number between 2 and 9 — what's the smallest number you can get down to? How many times did you have to divide? Could you do it any quicker by dividing by different numbers?

b) Repeat part **a)**, this time using different starting numbers.

c) Race your friends — see who can get to the smallest number with the fewest divisions.

Highest Common Factors

A common factor is a number that divides exactly into two or more different numbers.

The highest common factor (HCF) of a group of numbers is the largest common factor of those numbers. It's the biggest number that divides into all of them exactly.

> **Example 2**   **Find the highest common factor of 18 and 27.**
>
> 1. Write down the factors of 18 and 27:
>
>   factors of 18:
>   1, 2, 3, 6, 9, 18
>   factors of 27:
>   1, 3, 9, 27
>
> 2. The highest common factor is the biggest number that's in both lists.
>
>   HCF of 18 and 27 is **9**.

Exercise 2

1 **a)** Write down all the factors of 6.

   b) Write down all the factors of 24.

   c) Write down the common factors of 6 and 24 from your lists.

   d) Find the highest common factor — the biggest number in your list from part **c)**.

2 **a)** Write down all the factors of 10.

   b) Write down all the factors of 15.

   c) Find the highest common factor of 10 and 15.

3 **a)** Write down all the factors of 12.

   b) Write down all the factors of 25.

   c) Find the highest common factor of 12 and 25.

4 Find the highest common factor (HCF) of each of the following pairs of numbers.

   a) 4 and 16   **b)** 8 and 32

   c) 7 and 28   **d)** 5 and 35

   e) 6 and 24   **f)** 10 and 40

5 Find the HCF of each of the following pairs of numbers.

   a) 3 and 8   **b)** 4 and 15

   c) 8 and 21   **d)** 10 and 27

   e) 13 and 28   **f)** 9 and 32

6 Find the HCF of each of the following pairs of numbers.

   a) 8 and 12   **b)** 6 and 8

   c) 20 and 30   **d)** 14 and 35

   e) 9 and 24   **f)** 16 and 40

4.3 Prime Numbers

A prime number is a number that has no factors except itself and 1.

In other words, the only numbers that divide exactly into a prime number are itself and 1.

But remember... 1 is not a prime number.

Here are the first few prime numbers: 2, 3, 5, 7, 11, 13, 17, 19, 23, 29, ...

Example 1 | **Which of the numbers in the box are primes?**

| 37 | 38 | 39 | 40 | 41 |

1. Look for factors of each of the numbers.

2. If you can find factors, then the number isn't prime.

3. If there are no factors other than itself and 1, the number is prime.

$38 = 2 \times 19$, so 38 isn't prime
$39 = 3 \times 13$, so 39 isn't prime
$40 = 4 \times 10$, so 40 isn't prime

37 has no factors other than 1 and 37.
41 has no factors other than 1 and 41.

So the prime numbers are **37** and **41**.

Exercise 1

1 **a)** Find all the factors of the three numbers in the box.

| 30 | 31 | 32 |

   b) Which of the three numbers is a prime number?
Explain your answer.

2 Look at the list of numbers.

| 41 | 43 | 45 | 47 |

   a) Which number in the list is not prime?

   b) Explain how you know that this number is not prime.

3 **a)** Which three numbers in the box are not prime?

| 21 | 23 | 25 | 27 | 29 |

   b) Explain how you know that these numbers are not prime.

4 Write down the prime numbers from this list:

    7,   15,   23,   28,   35,   49,   53,   59.

5 **a)** Write down the four prime numbers between 10 and 20.

    b) Find the two prime numbers between 30 and 40.

6 **a)** Find the largest prime number that is less than 70.

    b) Find all the prime numbers between 40 and 50.

7 Explain why 42 is not a prime number.

8 Explain why 41 is a prime number.

9 Is 51 a prime number? Explain your answer.

10 Look at the numbers in the box.

71	72	73	74	75	76	77	78	79

Write down all the prime numbers in the box.

Investigate — Factor Trees

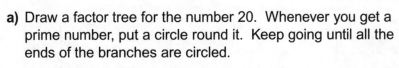

A factor tree splits up a number into branches of its factors, like the factor tree for 18 shown.

a) Draw a factor tree for the number 20. Whenever you get a prime number, put a circle round it. Keep going until all the ends of the branches are circled.

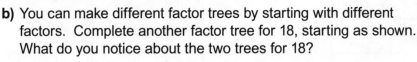

b) You can make different factor trees by starting with different factors. Complete another factor tree for 18, starting as shown. What do you notice about the two trees for 18?

c) Try and find all the different factor trees for 20.

d) Pick another starting number (e.g. 64, 100) and try and find all its factor trees.

Section 5 — Fractions and Percentages

5.1 Equivalent Fractions

Fraction Basics

Fractions tell you how many parts of a total you have.

The bottom number of a fraction tells you how many equal parts something is split into. It is called the denominator.

The top number tells you how many parts you have. It is called the numerator.

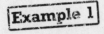 **What fraction of this shape is shaded?**

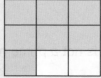

1. The shape is divided into 9 equal parts so the denominator is 9.

2. 7 parts are shaded so the numerator is 7.

The fraction shaded is $\frac{7}{9}$.

Exercise 1

1 Write down the fraction of each of these shapes that is shaded.

a)
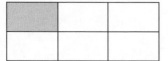

b)
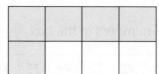

c)
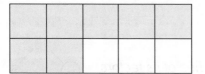

d)
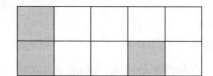

e)
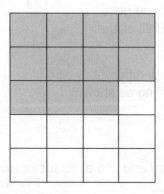

f)
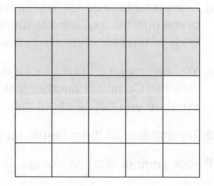

2 Copy each grid and shade to show the given fraction.

a) $\frac{7}{8}$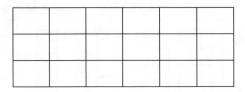

b) $\frac{5}{12}$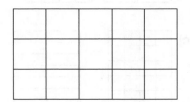

c) $\frac{12}{18}$

d) $\frac{11}{15}$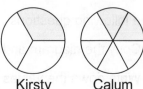

Investigate — Cake Fractions

Kirsty eats $\frac{1}{3}$ of a cake. Calum eats $\frac{2}{6}$ of a cake.

The amount of cake they each eat is the same — the fractions are just written in different ways. They're called equivalent fractions.

Kirsty   Calum

Find some other ways of dividing up the cake so that you could eat a third of it.

Equivalent Fractions

Equivalent fractions are fractions that are equal in size.

These two shapes are the same size and have an equal area shaded.

This means the fractions of the two shapes that are shaded are equivalent.

 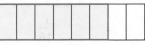

$\frac{3}{4}$ is equivalent to $\frac{6}{8}$

Example 2 **Write down the equivalent fractions shown in this diagram.**

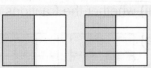

1. For each shape, write a fraction to show how much is shaded. Put the number of shaded squares as the numerator and the total number of squares as the denominator.

   Shape 1: $\frac{2}{4}$ Shape 2: $\frac{4}{8}$

2. If the same area of the two shapes is shaded, you can say that the fractions are equivalent.

   $\frac{2}{4}$ is equivalent to $\frac{4}{8}$

Exercise 2

1 Write down the equivalent fractions shown in each pair of diagrams.

a)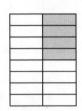

b)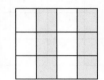

c)

d)

2 For the following questions:

   i) Copy the diagram and shade the shapes to make the fractions equivalent.

   ii) Write down the values of the missing letters.

a)

$$\frac{1}{4} \quad = \quad \frac{a}{8} \quad = \quad \frac{b}{16}$$

b)

$$\frac{3}{9} \quad = \quad \frac{c}{18} \quad = \quad \frac{d}{36}$$

3 For the pairs of shapes, write down **i)** the fraction of each shape that is shaded, and **ii)** whether the fractions are equivalent.

a)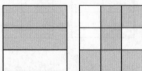

b)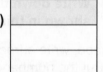

c)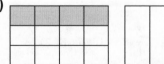

d)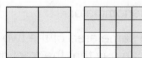

To find an equivalent fraction, you multiply or divide
the numerator and denominator by the same number.

Example 3 Find the value that replaces the star:

a) $\dfrac{5}{6} = \dfrac{\bigstar}{12}$.

1. Find what you need to multiply by to get from one denominator to the other.

2. To get from 6 to 12, multiply by 2.

3. Multiply the numerator by the same number to find the missing value.

$$\dfrac{5}{6} = \dfrac{\bigstar}{12}$$
$\times 2$

$\times 2$
$$\dfrac{5}{6} = \dfrac{10}{12}$$
So $\bigstar = 10$

b) $\dfrac{9}{18} = \dfrac{3}{\bigstar}$.

1. Find what you need to divide by to get from one numerator to the other.

2. To get from 9 to 3, divide by 3.

3. Divide the denominator by the same number to find $\bigstar$.

$\div 3$
$$\dfrac{9}{18} = \dfrac{3}{\bigstar}$$

$$\dfrac{9}{18} = \dfrac{3}{6}$$
So $\bigstar = 6$
$\div 3$

Exercise 3

1 Find the value of a in each of these pairs of equivalent fractions.

a) $\dfrac{2}{3} = \dfrac{a}{6}$

b) $\dfrac{1}{4} = \dfrac{a}{8}$

c) $\dfrac{1}{2} = \dfrac{a}{20}$

d) $\dfrac{2}{3} = \dfrac{a}{12}$

e) $\dfrac{12}{16} = \dfrac{a}{4}$

f) $\dfrac{20}{25} = \dfrac{a}{5}$

g) $\dfrac{6}{18} = \dfrac{a}{6}$

h) $\dfrac{9}{12} = \dfrac{a}{4}$

2 Find the value of a in each of these pairs of equivalent fractions.

a) $\dfrac{1}{2} = \dfrac{5}{a}$

b) $\dfrac{2}{3} = \dfrac{8}{a}$

c) $\dfrac{4}{5} = \dfrac{20}{a}$

d) $\dfrac{3}{7} = \dfrac{15}{a}$

e) $\dfrac{7}{9} = \dfrac{21}{a}$

f) $\dfrac{6}{14} = \dfrac{3}{a}$

g) $\dfrac{12}{16} = \dfrac{3}{a}$

h) $\dfrac{10}{16} = \dfrac{5}{a}$

3 Find the values of a and b in each of these sets of equivalent fractions.

a) $\dfrac{3}{4} = \dfrac{a}{8} = \dfrac{b}{16}$

b) $\dfrac{1}{3} = \dfrac{2}{a} = \dfrac{b}{18}$

c) $\dfrac{9}{24} = \dfrac{3}{a} = \dfrac{b}{16}$

d) $\dfrac{9}{15} = \dfrac{3}{a} = \dfrac{b}{20}$

Simplifying Fractions

Simplifying a fraction means writing an equivalent fraction using the smallest possible numbers.

Simplifying a fraction is also called cancelling down or 'writing a fraction in its simplest terms'.

Fractions can be put into a calculator using the fraction button — 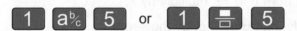.

For example, you can enter the fraction $\frac{1}{5}$ by pressing:

$$\boxed{1}\ \boxed{a^b_c}\ \boxed{5} \quad \text{or} \quad \boxed{1}\ \boxed{\frac{\square}{\square}}\ \boxed{5}$$

To simplify a fraction using your calculator, enter the fraction and then press the equals button.

Example 4

a) Write the fraction $\frac{24}{40}$ in its simplest terms.

1. Find a common factor of the top and bottom number:
   4 is a factor of both 24 and 40, so
   divide the top and bottom of the fraction by 4.

   $$\frac{24}{40} \overset{\div 4}{\underset{\div 4}{=}} \frac{6}{10}$$

2. Repeat Step 1 for the fraction $\frac{6}{10}$:

   2 is a factor of both 6 and 10, so
   divide the top and bottom of the fraction by 2.

   $$\frac{6}{10} \overset{\div 2}{\underset{\div 2}{=}} \frac{3}{5}$$

3. 3 and 5 have no common factors, so the fraction $\frac{3}{5}$ can't be simplified any further.

b) Simplify the fraction $\frac{16}{28}$ using your calculator.

1. Type the fraction into your calculator and hit the equals button.

2. The answer is the fraction in its simplest terms.

Exercise 4

Answer questions 1 to 5 **without** using a calculator.

1 Find the numbers that replace each shape to write these fractions in their simplest terms.

a)
$$\frac{4}{8} = \frac{1}{2}$$

b)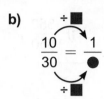
$$\frac{10}{30} = \frac{1}{\bullet}$$

c)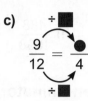
$$\frac{9}{12} = \frac{\bullet}{4}$$

2 a) Find a number greater than 1 which is a common factor of 3 and 12.

b) Divide 3 and 12 by your answer to part **a)** to write the fraction $\frac{3}{12}$ in its simplest terms.

3 a) Find a number greater than 1 which is a common factor of 21 and 28.

b) Divide 21 and 28 by your answer to part **a)** to write the fraction $\frac{21}{28}$ in its simplest terms.

4 Find the numbers that replace each shape to write these fractions in their simplest terms.

a) $\frac{8}{20} = \frac{4}{\bigstar} = \frac{2}{\pmb{(}}$

b) $\frac{12}{30} = \frac{6}{\bigstar} = \frac{\blacktriangle}{\pmb{(}}$

c) $\frac{18}{24} = \frac{\text{✦}}{8} = \frac{\blacktriangle}{\pmb{(}}$

d) $\frac{36}{42} = \frac{\text{✦}}{21} = \frac{\blacktriangle}{\pmb{(}}$

5 Write each fraction in its simplest terms.

a) $\frac{5}{10}$ **b)** $\frac{3}{12}$ **c)** $\frac{2}{8}$ **d)** $\frac{8}{10}$ **e)** $\frac{4}{40}$ **f)** $\frac{8}{24}$

g) $\frac{2}{20}$ **h)** $\frac{8}{26}$ **i)** $\frac{11}{22}$ **j)** $\frac{6}{9}$ **k)** $\frac{10}{15}$ **l)** $\frac{16}{24}$

m) $\frac{15}{27}$ **n)** $\frac{25}{40}$ **o)** $\frac{24}{32}$ **p)** $\frac{18}{42}$ **q)** $\frac{40}{60}$ **r)** $\frac{48}{56}$

6 Simplify these fractions using your calculator.

a) $\dfrac{56}{64}$　　b) $\dfrac{125}{350}$　　c) $\dfrac{153}{459}$　　d) $\dfrac{123}{492}$　　e) $\dfrac{382}{2000}$　　f) $\dfrac{90}{162}$

g) $\dfrac{246}{861}$　　h) $\dfrac{488}{1098}$　　i) $\dfrac{252}{420}$　　j) $\dfrac{350}{550}$　　k) $\dfrac{65}{156}$　　l) $\dfrac{99}{143}$

Common Denominators

Putting fractions over a <u>common denominator</u> means rewriting them so they both have the same <u>denominator</u>.

Example 5 Rewrite the fractions $\dfrac{1}{3}$ and $\dfrac{1}{6}$ so they have a common denominator.

1. For the common denominator, look for a number that both 3 and 6 divide into (go into) exactly.

　3 and 6 both go into 6

2. Rewrite $\dfrac{1}{3}$ as an equivalent fraction with 6 as the denominator by multiplying both the top and bottom by 2.

$$\dfrac{1}{3} = \dfrac{2}{6} \quad (\times 2)$$

3. Write out the two fractions again.

　$\dfrac{2}{6}$ and $\dfrac{1}{6}$.

Example 6 Rewrite the fractions $\dfrac{5}{6}$ and $\dfrac{3}{4}$ so they have a common denominator.

1. Look for a number that both 6 and 4 divide into exactly.

　6 and 4 both go into 12

2. Rewrite $\dfrac{5}{6}$ as an equivalent fraction with 12 as the denominator by multiplying both the top and bottom by 2.

$$\dfrac{5}{6} = \dfrac{10}{12} \quad (\times 2)$$

3. Rewrite $\dfrac{3}{4}$ as an equivalent fraction with 12 as the denominator by multiplying both the top and bottom by 3.

$$\dfrac{3}{4} = \dfrac{9}{12} \quad (\times 3)$$

4. Write out the two fractions again.

　$\dfrac{10}{12}$ and $\dfrac{9}{12}$.

Exercise 5

1 Rewrite the fractions $\frac{2}{3}$ and $\frac{1}{6}$ so they have a common denominator of 6.

2 Rewrite the fractions $\frac{3}{5}$ and $\frac{9}{10}$ so they have a common denominator of 10.

3 **a)** Find a number which is a multiple of both 2 and 8.

   b) Use your answer to rewrite the fractions $\frac{1}{2}$ and $\frac{3}{8}$ so they have a common denominator.

4 Rewrite these pairs of fractions so they have a common denominator.

   a) $\frac{3}{4}, \frac{3}{8}$ **b)** $\frac{1}{3}, \frac{7}{12}$ **c)** $\frac{1}{5}, \frac{11}{15}$ **d)** $\frac{4}{5}, \frac{3}{10}$

   e) $\frac{5}{6}, \frac{1}{3}$ **f)** $\frac{2}{3}, \frac{3}{15}$ **g)** $\frac{8}{10}, \frac{7}{20}$ **h)** $\frac{5}{6}, \frac{13}{18}$

   i) $\frac{1}{4}, \frac{17}{24}$ **j)** $\frac{17}{18}, \frac{4}{9}$ **k)** $\frac{21}{28}, \frac{2}{7}$ **l)** $\frac{12}{25}, \frac{3}{5}$

   m) $\frac{2}{5}, \frac{15}{40}$ **n)** $\frac{11}{30}, \frac{3}{10}$ **o)** $\frac{19}{42}, \frac{4}{7}$ **p)** $\frac{5}{8}, \frac{37}{56}$

5 Rewrite the fractions $\frac{1}{3}$ and $\frac{3}{4}$ so they have a common denominator of 12.

6 Rewrite the fractions $\frac{5}{6}$ and $\frac{7}{9}$ so they have a common denominator of 18.

7 **a)** Find a number which is a multiple of both 3 and 5.

   b) Use your answer to rewrite the fractions $\frac{2}{3}$ and $\frac{4}{5}$ so they have a common denominator.

8 **a)** Find a number which is a multiple of both 2 and 11.

   b) Use your answer to rewrite the fractions $\frac{1}{2}$ and $\frac{5}{11}$ so they have a common denominator.

9 Rewrite these pairs of fractions so they have a common denominator.

a) $\dfrac{1}{2}$, $\dfrac{2}{3}$

b) $\dfrac{3}{4}$, $\dfrac{2}{3}$

c) $\dfrac{2}{3}$, $\dfrac{5}{8}$

d) $\dfrac{5}{6}$, $\dfrac{1}{4}$

e) $\dfrac{1}{8}$, $\dfrac{7}{9}$

f) $\dfrac{4}{5}$, $\dfrac{3}{7}$

g) $\dfrac{10}{11}$, $\dfrac{1}{3}$

h) $\dfrac{7}{10}$, $\dfrac{9}{15}$

i) $\dfrac{1}{7}$, $\dfrac{5}{6}$

10 a) Find the fraction equivalent to $\dfrac{1}{2}$ which has a denominator of 24.

b) Find the fraction equivalent to $\dfrac{5}{6}$ which has a denominator of 24.

c) Use your answers to rewrite the fractions $\dfrac{1}{2}$, $\dfrac{5}{6}$ and $\dfrac{19}{24}$ so they have a common denominator.

11 a) Find the fraction equivalent to $\dfrac{5}{6}$ which has a denominator of 18.

b) Find the fraction equivalent to $\dfrac{2}{9}$ which has a denominator of 18.

c) Use your answers to rewrite the fractions $\dfrac{5}{6}$, $\dfrac{2}{9}$ and $\dfrac{3}{18}$ so they have a common denominator.

12 Rewrite these sets of fractions so they have a common denominator.

a) $\dfrac{1}{3}$, $\dfrac{2}{5}$, $\dfrac{9}{15}$

b) $\dfrac{1}{2}$, $\dfrac{3}{4}$, $\dfrac{7}{16}$

c) $\dfrac{3}{4}$, $\dfrac{3}{5}$, $\dfrac{17}{20}$

d) $\dfrac{1}{3}$, $\dfrac{7}{8}$, $\dfrac{21}{24}$

e) $\dfrac{3}{7}$, $\dfrac{2}{3}$, $\dfrac{12}{21}$

f) $\dfrac{5}{7}$, $\dfrac{3}{4}$, $\dfrac{5}{28}$

g) $\dfrac{4}{5}$, $\dfrac{6}{7}$, $\dfrac{20}{35}$

h) $\dfrac{9}{10}$, $\dfrac{3}{5}$, $\dfrac{33}{40}$

i) $\dfrac{1}{6}$, $\dfrac{29}{42}$, $\dfrac{5}{7}$

13 Write the following sets of fractions so they have a common denominator.

a) $\dfrac{4}{9}$, $\dfrac{7}{12}$, and $\dfrac{5}{6}$

b) $\dfrac{5}{16}$, $\dfrac{3}{8}$, and $\dfrac{7}{12}$

Ordering Fractions

Fractions can be ordered by size, even if they have different <u>denominators</u>.
It makes it easier if you rewrite them with a <u>common denominator</u>.

Example 7 Write the fractions $\frac{1}{3}$, $\frac{3}{4}$ and $\frac{7}{12}$ in order, from smallest to largest, and show them on a number line.

1. Find a common denominator — a number that 3, 4 and 12 all divide into exactly.

   3, 4 and 12 all go into 12

   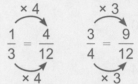

2. Rewrite the fractions with the common denominator.

3. Look at the numerators to put the fractions in order.

   $\frac{4}{12}$ $\quad$ $\frac{7}{12}$ $\quad$ $\frac{9}{12}$

4. Write the ordered fractions back in their original form.

   $\frac{1}{3}$ $\quad$ $\frac{7}{12}$ $\quad$ $\frac{3}{4}$

5. Split a number line between 0 and 1 into 12 equal sections (the common denominator). To show the fractions on the number line, count up from 0 using the numerators from step 3 (4, 7 and 9).

   There are 12 spaces from 0 to 1, so each dash represents $\frac{1}{12}$.

   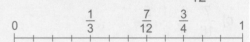

Exercise 6

1 Put the following fractions in order on a number line: $\frac{5}{9}$, $\frac{2}{9}$, $\frac{8}{9}$

2 **a)** Find the fraction equivalent to $\frac{2}{3}$ which has a denominator of 12.

   b) Use your answer to write down which fraction is bigger: $\frac{2}{3}$ or $\frac{9}{12}$.

3 **a)** Rewrite the fractions $\frac{3}{4}$ and $\frac{27}{32}$ so they have a common denominator of 32.

   b) Use your answer to write down which fraction is bigger: $\frac{3}{4}$ or $\frac{27}{32}$.

4 **a)** Rewrite the fractions $\frac{1}{3}$ and $\frac{3}{5}$ so they have a common denominator of 15.

   b) Use your answer to write the fractions $\frac{1}{3}$, $\frac{3}{5}$ and $\frac{4}{15}$ in order, from smallest to largest.

5 **a)** Rewrite the fractions $\frac{5}{6}$ and $\frac{1}{4}$ so they have a common denominator of 12.

b) Use your answer to write the fractions $\frac{5}{6}$, $\frac{1}{4}$ and $\frac{2}{12}$ in order, from smallest to largest.

6 By rewriting the fractions so they have a common denominator of 20, put these groups of fractions in order, from smallest to largest.

a) $\frac{1}{2}$, $\frac{3}{5}$, $\frac{7}{20}$

b) $\frac{7}{10}$, $\frac{2}{5}$, $\frac{11}{20}$

c) $\frac{13}{20}$, $\frac{1}{4}$, $\frac{4}{5}$

d) $\frac{7}{10}$, $\frac{3}{20}$, $\frac{1}{2}$

7 By rewriting the fractions so they have a common denominator of 18, put these groups of fractions in order, from smallest to largest.

a) $\frac{7}{18}$, $\frac{1}{3}$, $\frac{5}{9}$

b) $\frac{5}{6}$, $\frac{4}{9}$, $\frac{11}{18}$

c) $\frac{7}{18}$, $\frac{8}{9}$, $\frac{1}{2}$, $\frac{5}{6}$

d) $\frac{2}{3}$, $\frac{4}{9}$, $\frac{13}{18}$, $\frac{1}{6}$

8 Put these groups of fractions in order, from smallest to largest.

a) $\frac{3}{4}$, $\frac{11}{16}$, $\frac{5}{8}$

b) $\frac{5}{24}$, $\frac{1}{6}$, $\frac{7}{8}$

c) $\frac{5}{6}$, $\frac{4}{15}$, $\frac{19}{30}$

d) $\frac{1}{2}$, $\frac{5}{16}$, $\frac{4}{16}$, $\frac{3}{8}$

e) $\frac{2}{4}$, $\frac{23}{28}$, $\frac{5}{7}$, $\frac{3}{4}$

f) $\frac{5}{8}$, $\frac{15}{32}$, $\frac{3}{16}$, $\frac{24}{32}$

9 For each group of fractions:
   i) put them in order, from smallest to largest, and
   ii) show them on a number line between 0 and 1.

a) $\frac{1}{15}$, $\frac{2}{5}$, $\frac{1}{3}$, $\frac{3}{15}$, $\frac{3}{5}$

b) $\frac{5}{8}$, $\frac{17}{24}$, $\frac{1}{3}$, $\frac{20}{24}$, $\frac{2}{3}$

c) $\frac{1}{4}$, $\frac{4}{8}$, $\frac{3}{4}$, $\frac{7}{8}$, $\frac{11}{16}$

d) $\frac{7}{10}$, $\frac{6}{10}$, $\frac{13}{20}$, $\frac{3}{4}$, $\frac{1}{4}$

5.2 Adding and Subtracting Fractions

Fractions with the Same Denominator

Fractions with a common denominator can be added or subtracted
by adding or subtracting the numerators.

$\frac{2}{7}$ can be added to $\frac{3}{7}$ to give $\frac{5}{7}$:

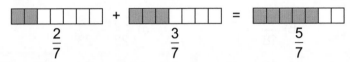

$$\frac{2}{7} \quad + \quad \frac{3}{7} \quad = \quad \frac{5}{7}$$

Example 1 Work out $\frac{3}{11} + \frac{4}{11}$.

The denominators are the same,
so add the numerators.

$$\frac{3}{11} + \frac{4}{11} = \frac{3+4}{11} = \frac{7}{11}$$

Example 2 Work out $\frac{7}{12} - \frac{4}{12}$. **Give your answer in its simplest terms.**

1. The denominators are the same,
   so subtract the numerators.

$$\frac{7}{12} - \frac{4}{12} = \frac{7-4}{12} = \frac{3}{12}$$

2. Simplify the fraction by dividing
   the top and bottom number by 3.

$$\overset{\div 3}{\frac{3}{12} = \frac{1}{4}}_{\div 3}$$

Exercise 1

Don't use a calculator for this exercise.

1 Copy and complete these calculations.

a) $\frac{2}{9} + \frac{2}{9} = \frac{2+2}{9} = \frac{}{9}$

b) $\frac{5}{8} + \frac{2}{8} = \frac{5+}{8} = \frac{}{8}$

c) $\frac{6}{7} - \frac{3}{7} = \frac{-3}{7} = \frac{}{7}$

2 Add these pairs of fractions.

a) $\frac{2}{8} + \frac{3}{8}$

b) $\frac{5}{7} + \frac{1}{7}$

c) $\frac{4}{11} + \frac{6}{11}$

d) $\frac{2}{10} + \frac{5}{10}$

e) $\frac{2}{6} + \frac{3}{6}$

f) $\frac{6}{12} + \frac{1}{12}$

g) $\frac{9}{13} + \frac{2}{13}$

h) $\frac{3}{13} + \frac{5}{13}$

i) $\frac{7}{16} + \frac{8}{16}$

j) $\frac{5}{21} + \frac{12}{21}$

3 Subtract these pairs of fractions.

a) $\dfrac{8}{9} - \dfrac{7}{9}$ 　　 b) $\dfrac{8}{13} - \dfrac{5}{13}$ 　　 c) $\dfrac{4}{5} - \dfrac{2}{5}$ 　　 d) $\dfrac{5}{7} - \dfrac{2}{7}$ 　　 e) $\dfrac{3}{8} - \dfrac{2}{8}$

f) $\dfrac{11}{15} - \dfrac{4}{15}$ 　　 g) $\dfrac{12}{16} - \dfrac{3}{16}$ 　　 h) $\dfrac{11}{13} - \dfrac{10}{13}$ 　　 i) $\dfrac{16}{17} - \dfrac{9}{17}$ 　　 j) $\dfrac{15}{21} - \dfrac{8}{21}$

4 Work out these calculations.

a) $\dfrac{7}{12} + \dfrac{4}{12}$ 　　 b) $\dfrac{11}{18} - \dfrac{4}{18}$ 　　 c) $\dfrac{21}{23} - \dfrac{18}{23}$

d) $\dfrac{9}{19} + \dfrac{7}{19}$ 　　 e) $\dfrac{18}{22} - \dfrac{9}{22}$ 　　 f) $\dfrac{7}{16} + \dfrac{6}{16}$

5 Work out these calculations. Give your answers in their simplest terms.

a) $\dfrac{2}{6} + \dfrac{2}{6}$ 　　 b) $\dfrac{6}{8} - \dfrac{2}{8}$ 　　 c) $\dfrac{5}{10} + \dfrac{3}{10}$ 　　 d) $\dfrac{3}{9} + \dfrac{3}{9}$ 　　 e) $\dfrac{10}{12} - \dfrac{2}{12}$

f) $\dfrac{13}{15} - \dfrac{3}{15}$ 　　 g) $\dfrac{11}{12} - \dfrac{7}{12}$ 　　 h) $\dfrac{3}{16} + \dfrac{5}{16}$ 　　 i) $\dfrac{20}{30} + \dfrac{4}{30}$ 　　 j) $\dfrac{11}{28} + \dfrac{10}{28}$

6 Eric eats $\dfrac{5}{21}$ of a cake on Monday and another $\dfrac{11}{21}$ of the cake on Tuesday.
What fraction of the cake has he eaten in total?

7 Melissa has $\dfrac{29}{35}$ metres of thread. She uses $\dfrac{21}{35}$ metres to make a bracelet.
How much thread has she got left?

8 Hasan has some letters to write.
He writes $\dfrac{7}{18}$ of the letters on Saturday and $\dfrac{4}{18}$ of them on Sunday.
What fraction of the letters has he written so far?

9 Jason and Charlotte are sharing a pizza.
Jason eats $\dfrac{4}{9}$ of the pizza and Charlotte eats $\dfrac{3}{9}$.
What fraction of the pizza is left over?

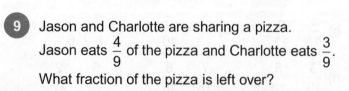

Different Denominators

Fractions with different <u>denominators</u> can also be added and subtracted. You need to rewrite them with a <u>common denominator</u> first, before adding or subtracting the <u>numerators</u>.

Example 3 Work out $\dfrac{3}{8} + \dfrac{1}{4}$.

1. Rewrite $\dfrac{1}{4}$ with a denominator of 8 by multiplying the top and bottom by 2.

2. Now the fractions have a common denominator, so add the numerators.

$$\overset{\times 2}{\overset{\frown}{\dfrac{1}{4}}} = \dfrac{2}{8}$$
$$\underset{\times 2}{\underset{\smile}{}}$$

$$\dfrac{3}{8} + \dfrac{2}{8} = \dfrac{3+2}{8} = \dfrac{5}{8}$$

Exercise 2

Don't use a calculator for this exercise.

1 Copy and complete these calculations.

a) $\dfrac{1}{6} + \dfrac{1}{3} = \dfrac{1}{6} + \dfrac{}{6} = \dfrac{}{6}$

b) $\dfrac{5}{9} + \dfrac{1}{3} = \dfrac{5}{9} + \dfrac{}{9} = \dfrac{}{9}$

c) $\dfrac{5}{6} - \dfrac{3}{12} = \dfrac{}{12} - \dfrac{3}{12} = \dfrac{}{12}$

d) $\dfrac{11}{12} - \dfrac{1}{3} = \dfrac{11}{12} - \dfrac{}{12} = \dfrac{}{12}$

2 a) Rewrite the fractions $\dfrac{2}{3}$ and $\dfrac{3}{15}$ so they have a common denominator.

b) Use your answer to **a)** to work out $\dfrac{2}{3} + \dfrac{3}{15}$.

3 a) Rewrite the fractions $\dfrac{3}{5}$ and $\dfrac{1}{4}$ so they have a common denominator.

b) Use your answer to **a)** to work out $\dfrac{3}{5} - \dfrac{1}{4}$.

4 Add or subtract these fractions by first rewriting them so they have a common denominator. Give your answers in their simplest terms.

a) $\dfrac{1}{6} + \dfrac{4}{12}$

b) $\dfrac{3}{5} + \dfrac{2}{10}$

c) $\dfrac{3}{4} - \dfrac{5}{12}$

d) $\dfrac{8}{16} - \dfrac{1}{4}$

e) $\dfrac{1}{6} + \dfrac{3}{24}$

f) $\dfrac{17}{20} - \dfrac{3}{4}$

g) $\dfrac{3}{5} + \dfrac{9}{25}$

h) $\dfrac{10}{22} + \dfrac{3}{11}$

5 Add or subtract these fractions by first rewriting them so they have a common denominator. Simplify your answers where possible.

a) $\dfrac{3}{4} + \dfrac{1}{6}$ 　　　 b) $\dfrac{7}{8} - \dfrac{1}{6}$ 　　　 c) $\dfrac{1}{2} + \dfrac{1}{5}$ 　　　 d) $\dfrac{3}{5} - \dfrac{2}{6}$

e) $\dfrac{1}{7} + \dfrac{4}{6}$ 　　　 f) $\dfrac{4}{5} - \dfrac{2}{8}$ 　　　 g) $\dfrac{6}{7} - \dfrac{2}{5}$ 　　　 h) $\dfrac{3}{4} - \dfrac{3}{7}$

6 In a shop, $\dfrac{4}{15}$ of the kites are red and $\dfrac{2}{5}$ are blue.

What is the total fraction, in its simplest form, of kites that are either red or blue?

7 Josie has a ribbon that is $\dfrac{4}{5}$ m long. She cuts off $\dfrac{2}{7}$ m of the ribbon.

How long is the ribbon now? Give your answer as a fraction in its simplest form.

8 Jack is baking. He puts $\dfrac{7}{8}$ kg of sugar in a bowl.

He removes $\dfrac{3}{6}$ kg of the sugar and replaces it with butter.

How much sugar is left in the bowl?
Give your answer as a fraction in its simplest form.

> ### Investigate — Top-Heavy Fractions
>
> Whole numbers can also be written as fractions,
> e.g. you can write 1 as $\dfrac{1}{1}$ and 2 as $\dfrac{2}{1}$.
>
> a) How would you write other whole numbers as fractions?
> Try it for 3, 4, 5, etc.
>
> b) Using what you know about equivalent fractions, write down some other ways of writing whole numbers as fractions, by writing them with different denominators.
>
> c) Write 1 as a fraction with denominator 2. Using this, how would you write $1 + \dfrac{1}{2}$ as a fraction?
>
> d) Now write 2 as a fraction with denominator 4. How would you write $2 + \dfrac{1}{4}$? Make up some more examples like this.

5.3 Multiplying and Dividing Fractions

Multiplying Whole Numbers by Fractions

To multiply a whole number by a fraction:
- multiply by the <u>numerator</u>
- divide by the <u>denominator</u>

You can do these steps in any order.

Example 1 Work out $10 \times \dfrac{2}{5}$

1. Multiply by the numerator — so multiply 10 by 2.

$$10 \times \frac{2}{5} = \frac{10 \times 2}{5} = \frac{20}{5}$$

2. Divide by the denominator — so divide the result by 5.

$$= 20 \div 5 = 4$$

(You could also divide 10 by 5 first, then multiply the result by 2. You'll get the same answer.)

Example 2 Find $\dfrac{2}{3}$ of 15.

1. 'Of' means '×', so multiply $\dfrac{2}{3}$ by 15.

$$\frac{2}{3} \times 15$$

2. Divide 15 by the denominator (3), then multiply the result by the numerator (2).

$$15 \div 3 = 5$$
$$5 \times 2 = 10$$

Exercise 1

Don't use a calculator for this exercise.

1 Work out these multiplications.

a) $9 \times \dfrac{1}{3}$ **b)** $8 \times \dfrac{1}{2}$ **c)** $16 \times \dfrac{1}{4}$

d) $21 \times \dfrac{1}{3}$ **e)** $32 \times \dfrac{1}{8}$ **f)** $36 \times \dfrac{1}{9}$

g) $24 \times \dfrac{1}{4}$ **h)** $35 \times \dfrac{1}{7}$ **i)** $33 \times \dfrac{1}{11}$

2 Copy and complete these calculations.

a) $12 \times \dfrac{3}{4} = \dfrac{12 \times 3}{4} = \dfrac{}{4} = \ldots\ldots$

b) $20 \times \dfrac{2}{5} = \dfrac{20 \times}{5} = \dfrac{}{5} = \ldots\ldots$

c) $9 \times \dfrac{2}{9} = \dfrac{\times}{9} = \dfrac{}{} = \ldots\ldots$

d) $6 \times \dfrac{5}{6} = \dfrac{\times}{} = \dfrac{}{} = \ldots\ldots$

3 Work out these multiplications. Give your answers in their simplest terms.

a) $6 \times \dfrac{2}{3}$

b) $4 \times \dfrac{3}{6}$

c) $8 \times \dfrac{3}{4}$

d) $9 \times \dfrac{4}{6}$

e) $7 \times \dfrac{4}{14}$

f) $10 \times \dfrac{4}{20}$

g) $12 \times \dfrac{3}{9}$

h) $11 \times \dfrac{5}{11}$

i) $9 \times \dfrac{4}{12}$

j) $16 \times \dfrac{2}{8}$

k) $15 \times \dfrac{4}{10}$

l) $20 \times \dfrac{3}{5}$

4 Find:

a) $\dfrac{1}{4}$ of 16

b) $\dfrac{1}{5}$ of 15

c) $\dfrac{3}{4}$ of 12

d) $\dfrac{4}{5}$ of 20

e) $\dfrac{3}{8}$ of 24

f) $\dfrac{5}{6}$ of 6

g) $\dfrac{2}{8}$ of 32

h) $\dfrac{4}{6}$ of 9

i) $\dfrac{3}{5}$ of 25

5 Raju has 44 sweets. He gives $\dfrac{3}{11}$ of them to his sister.

How many sweets does Raju give to his sister?

6 Trudi is knitting a scarf. She wants it to be 90 cm long. She has knitted $\dfrac{2}{9}$ of it so far.

What length of the scarf has she knitted so far?

Multiplying Fractions by Fractions

To multiply one fraction by another fraction, multiply the <u>numerators</u> together and the <u>denominators</u> together separately.

Example 3   Work out $\frac{3}{8} \times \frac{2}{3}$.

1. Multiply the numerators.

2. Multiply the denominators.

$$\frac{3}{8} \times \frac{2}{3} = \frac{3 \times 2}{8 \times 3} = \frac{6}{24}$$

3. Simplify the fraction by dividing the top and bottom number by 6.

$$\overset{\div 6}{\frown} \\ \frac{6}{24} = \frac{1}{4} \\ \underset{\div 6}{\smile}$$

Exercise 2

Answer these questions **without using a calculator**.

1   Copy and complete these calculations.

a) $\frac{1}{3} \times \frac{1}{4} = \frac{1 \times 1}{3 \times 4} = \underline{\quad}$

b) $\frac{1}{3} \times \frac{1}{5} = \frac{1 \times 1}{3 \times 5} = \underline{\quad}$

c) $\frac{3}{4} \times \frac{1}{7} = \frac{3 \times}{4 \times} = \underline{\quad}$

d) $\frac{2}{5} \times \frac{3}{5} = \frac{\times 3}{\times 5} = \underline{\quad}$

e) $\frac{5}{9} \times \frac{1}{4} = \frac{\times 1}{9 \times} = \underline{\quad}$

f) $\frac{1}{9} \times \frac{1}{8} = \frac{1 \times}{\times} = \underline{\quad}$

g) $\frac{1}{7} \times \frac{4}{5} = \frac{1 \times}{\times} = \underline{\quad}$

h) $\frac{3}{7} \times \frac{4}{5} = \frac{\times}{\times} = \underline{\quad}$

2   Work out these multiplications.

a) $\frac{1}{3} \times \frac{5}{7}$ b) $\frac{1}{4} \times \frac{1}{4}$ c) $\frac{1}{3} \times \frac{2}{9}$ d) $\frac{3}{4} \times \frac{1}{8}$ e) $\frac{3}{5} \times \frac{1}{8}$

f) $\frac{1}{6} \times \frac{1}{3}$ g) $\frac{1}{5} \times \frac{4}{7}$ h) $\frac{2}{3} \times \frac{2}{5}$ i) $\frac{1}{4} \times \frac{1}{9}$ j) $\frac{2}{5} \times \frac{1}{7}$

3 Work out these multiplications.

a) $\dfrac{4}{7} \times \dfrac{2}{3}$ b) $\dfrac{3}{5} \times \dfrac{4}{9}$ c) $\dfrac{5}{7} \times \dfrac{6}{7}$ d) $\dfrac{5}{7} \times \dfrac{5}{6}$

4 Work out these multiplications. Give your answers in their simplest terms.

a) $\dfrac{2}{5} \times \dfrac{3}{4}$ b) $\dfrac{1}{4} \times \dfrac{4}{6}$ c) $\dfrac{2}{4} \times \dfrac{3}{12}$ d) $\dfrac{1}{2} \times \dfrac{8}{9}$ e) $\dfrac{3}{3} \times \dfrac{2}{6}$

f) $\dfrac{1}{4} \times \dfrac{4}{7}$ g) $\dfrac{5}{7} \times \dfrac{1}{5}$ h) $\dfrac{2}{3} \times \dfrac{2}{10}$ i) $\dfrac{5}{9} \times \dfrac{3}{5}$ j) $\dfrac{4}{5} \times \dfrac{5}{10}$

Dividing Fractions

To divide by a fraction, you multiply by its reciprocal.
You get the reciprocal by swapping around the numerator and the denominator.

Example 4   **Find the reciprocal of:**   a) $\dfrac{5}{7}$ b) $\dfrac{1}{9}$ c) **4**

1. Swap the numerator and denominator.   a) The reciprocal of $\dfrac{5}{7}$ is $\dfrac{7}{5}$

2. If the numerator of the fraction is 1, the reciprocal is a whole number.   b) The reciprocal of $\dfrac{1}{9}$ is $\dfrac{9}{1} = 9$

3. The reciprocal of a whole number is a fraction with numerator 1.   c) $4 = \dfrac{4}{1}$, so the reciprocal of 4 is $\dfrac{1}{4}$

Example 5   **Work out:**

a) $\dfrac{1}{3} \div \dfrac{2}{5}$ Multiply $\dfrac{1}{3}$ by the reciprocal of $\dfrac{2}{5}$. $\dfrac{1}{3} \times \dfrac{5}{2} = \dfrac{1 \times 5}{3 \times 2} = \dfrac{5}{6}$

b) $\dfrac{2}{7} \div 3$ Multiply $\dfrac{2}{7}$ by the reciprocal of 3.

     3 is the same as $\dfrac{3}{1}$, so its reciprocal is $\dfrac{1}{3}$. $\dfrac{2}{7} \times \dfrac{1}{3} = \dfrac{2 \times 1}{7 \times 3} = \dfrac{2}{21}$

Exercise 3

Answer these questions **without using a calculator**.

1 Find the reciprocal of these fractions.

a) $\dfrac{5}{6}$ b) $\dfrac{2}{3}$ c) $\dfrac{1}{9}$ d) $\dfrac{4}{9}$ e) $\dfrac{3}{10}$ f) $\dfrac{1}{6}$

g) $\dfrac{2}{7}$ h) $\dfrac{4}{11}$ i) $\dfrac{3}{5}$ j) $\dfrac{5}{8}$ k) $\dfrac{3}{4}$ l) $\dfrac{1}{10}$

2 Find the reciprocal of these numbers.

a) 3   b) 7   c) 6   d) 4   e) 9   f) 11

g) 5   h) 2   i) 10   j) 8   k) 15   l) 21

3 Copy and complete these calculations. You do not need to simplify your answers.

a) $\dfrac{1}{8} \div \dfrac{1}{4} = \dfrac{1}{8} \times \dfrac{4}{1} = \dfrac{1 \times 4}{8 \times 1} = \underline{}$ b) $\dfrac{2}{5} \div \dfrac{1}{2} = \dfrac{2}{5} \times \dfrac{2}{1} = \dfrac{2 \times 2}{5 \times 1} = \underline{}$

c) $\dfrac{1}{4} \div \dfrac{5}{6} = \dfrac{1}{4} \times \dfrac{}{5} = \dfrac{1 \times }{4 \times 5} = \underline{}$ d) $\dfrac{4}{7} \div \dfrac{2}{3} = \dfrac{4}{7} \times \dfrac{3}{} = \dfrac{4 \times 3}{7 \times } = \underline{}$

e) $\dfrac{3}{8} \div \dfrac{1}{2} = \dfrac{3}{8} \times \dfrac{}{} = \dfrac{3 \times }{8 \times } = \underline{}$ f) $\dfrac{1}{9} \div \dfrac{3}{8} = \dfrac{1}{9} \times \dfrac{}{} = \dfrac{1 \times }{9 \times } = \underline{}$

4 Work out these calculations. Give your answers in their simplest terms.

a) $\dfrac{1}{3} \div \dfrac{3}{8}$ b) $\dfrac{2}{5} \div \dfrac{1}{2}$ c) $\dfrac{1}{4} \div \dfrac{4}{5}$

d) $\dfrac{3}{11} \div \dfrac{11}{12}$ e) $\dfrac{4}{15} \div \dfrac{2}{3}$ f) $\dfrac{3}{30} \div \dfrac{3}{20}$

5 Copy and complete these calculations.

a) $3 \div \dfrac{3}{5} = 3 \times \dfrac{5}{3} = \dfrac{3 \times 5}{3} = \dfrac{}{3} = \dots\dots$

b) $4 \div \dfrac{2}{6} = 4 \times \dfrac{6}{} = \dfrac{4 \times 6}{} = \dfrac{}{} = \dots\dots$

6 Work out these calculations. Give your answers in their simplest terms.

a) $11 \div \dfrac{3}{9}$ **b)** $7 \div \dfrac{2}{6}$ **c)** $5 \div \dfrac{5}{6}$ **d)** $3 \div \dfrac{4}{12}$ **e)** $12 \div \dfrac{3}{5}$

7 Copy and complete these calculations.

a) $\dfrac{5}{6} \div 4 = \dfrac{5}{6} \times \dfrac{}{} = \dfrac{5 \times}{6 \times} = \dfrac{}{}$ **b)** $\dfrac{7}{8} \div 6 = \dfrac{7}{8} \times \dfrac{}{} = \dfrac{7 \times}{8 \times} = \dfrac{}{}$

8 Work out these calculations. Give your answers in their simplest terms.

a) $\dfrac{5}{6} \div 5$ **b)** $\dfrac{6}{9} \div 2$ **c)** $\dfrac{10}{12} \div 5$ **d)** $\dfrac{5}{8} \div 10$ **e)** $\dfrac{3}{11} \div 9$

9 $\dfrac{5}{7}$ of a cake is left over after a party. It is divided out equally between 5 people.

Work out what fraction of the cake each person gets, in its simplest form.

10 Adi buys a piece of rope which is $\dfrac{4}{5}$ m long. He cuts the rope into 8 equal parts.

Work out the length of each piece of rope as a fraction in its simplest form.

11 Faye wins some money. She wants to give $\dfrac{8}{9}$ of it to charity.

She chooses 4 charities and splits the money equally between them.
Work out what fraction of the money each of the charities gets.

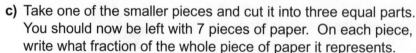

> ## Investigate — Paper Fractions
>
> **a)** Find a plain piece of paper and cut it into three equal parts.
>   Each part is a third of the whole piece.
>
> **b)** Now cut one of the thirds into three equal parts.
>   What fraction of the whole is one of these smaller parts?
>
> **c)** Take one of the smaller pieces and cut it into three equal parts.
>   You should now be left with 7 pieces of paper. On each piece,
>   write what fraction of the whole piece of paper it represents.
>
> **d)** Check you've got the fractions right by adding them all up to make 1.
>
> **e)** Start with new pieces of paper and cut them into different numbers
>   of parts. Check that the fractions add up to 1 each time.

5.4 Changing Fractions to Decimals and Percentages

Fractions and Decimals

Fractions and decimals are both ways of showing a proportion of something.
Any fraction can be written as a decimal.
You can do this by dividing the numerator by the denominator.

Example 1 Use a calculator to find $\frac{3}{8}$ as a decimal.

Divide 3 by 8 on the calculator. $\boxed{3}\ \boxed{\div}\ \boxed{8}$ = **0.375**

It's easier to write fractions as decimals when the denominator is 10, 100 or 1000.

Remember: $\frac{1}{10} = 0.1$ $\frac{1}{100} = 0.01$ $\frac{1}{1000} = 0.001$

Just put the numerator digits in the right decimal places.

$$\frac{135}{1000} = 0.135$$

tenths   hundredths   thousandths

Example 2   Write the following fractions as decimals:

a) $\frac{6}{10}$

This is the same as 6 tenths, so
write 6 in the tenths column. $\frac{6}{10} = \mathbf{0.6}$

b) $\frac{3}{100}$

This is the same as 3 hundredths,
so write 3 in the hundredths column. $\frac{3}{100} = \mathbf{0.03}$

c) $\frac{67}{1000}$

This is 67 thousandths, so line up the digits
so the 7 is in the thousandths column. $\frac{67}{1000} = \mathbf{0.067}$

Exercise 1

1 Use your calculator to write these fractions as decimals.
Do not round your answers.

a) $\dfrac{5}{8}$　　b) $\dfrac{5}{32}$　　c) $\dfrac{11}{25}$　　d) $\dfrac{9}{40}$　　e) $\dfrac{9}{16}$　　f) $\dfrac{1}{16}$

g) $\dfrac{7}{16}$　　h) $\dfrac{9}{50}$　　i) $\dfrac{7}{125}$　　j) $\dfrac{9}{375}$　　k) $\dfrac{11}{250}$　　l) $\dfrac{93}{625}$

m) $\dfrac{10}{32}$　　n) $\dfrac{17}{25}$　　o) $\dfrac{22}{64}$　　p) $\dfrac{18}{125}$　　q) $\dfrac{201}{250}$　　r) $\dfrac{480}{750}$

Answer questions 2 and 3 **without using a calculator**.

2 Copy and complete these conversions:

a) $\dfrac{9}{10}$ = ... tenths = 0.9

b) $\dfrac{5}{100}$ = 5 .... = 0.05

c) $\dfrac{16}{1000}$ = ... thousandths = ...

d) $\dfrac{98}{100}$ = 98 .... = ...

e) $\dfrac{83}{100}$ = ... hundredths = ...

f) $\dfrac{123}{1000}$ = 123 .... = ...

3 Write these fractions as decimals.

a) $\dfrac{4}{10}$　　b) $\dfrac{8}{10}$　　c) $\dfrac{2}{10}$　　d) $\dfrac{3}{10}$

e) $\dfrac{4}{100}$　　f) $\dfrac{6}{100}$　　g) $\dfrac{81}{100}$　　h) $\dfrac{14}{100}$

i) $\dfrac{26}{100}$　　j) $\dfrac{2}{1000}$　　k) $\dfrac{5}{1000}$　　l) $\dfrac{57}{1000}$

m) $\dfrac{39}{1000}$　　n) $\dfrac{391}{1000}$　　o) $\dfrac{998}{1000}$　　p) $\dfrac{17}{1000}$

If the fraction has a denominator which is a <u>factor</u> or <u>multiple</u> of 10, 100 or 1000, find the <u>equivalent fraction</u> with a denominator of 10, 100 or 1000 first. Then it's easy to change it into a decimal.

Example 3 Write $\dfrac{2}{5}$ as a decimal.

1. First, find a fraction equivalent to $\dfrac{2}{5}$ which has 10, 100 or 1000 as the denominator.

2. Multiply the numerator and denominator by 2 to rewrite the fraction with denominator 10.

$$\dfrac{2}{5} \xrightarrow{\times 2} \dfrac{4}{10} \xleftarrow{\times 2}$$

3. Change the fraction to a decimal.

$$\dfrac{4}{10} = 4 \text{ tenths}$$
$$= 0.4$$

---

4 **a)** Find the value of a if $\dfrac{4}{20} = \dfrac{a}{10}$.

 b) Use your answer to **a)** to write the fraction $\dfrac{4}{20}$ as a decimal.

5 **a)** Find a fraction equivalent to $\dfrac{12}{20}$ which has a denominator of 10.

 b) Use your answer to write $\dfrac{12}{20}$ as a decimal.

6 For each of these fractions:

 i) rewrite the fraction so that it has a denominator of 10, and

 ii) write the fraction as a decimal.

 a) $\dfrac{4}{5}$ **b)** $\dfrac{1}{5}$ **c)** $\dfrac{3}{5}$

 d) $\dfrac{18}{20}$ **e)** $\dfrac{10}{20}$ **f)** $\dfrac{9}{30}$

7 **a)** Find a fraction equivalent to $\dfrac{11}{50}$ which has a denominator of 100.

 b) Use your answer to write $\dfrac{11}{50}$ as a decimal.

You can change a decimal to a fraction by writing it as a fraction with a denominator of 10, 100 or 1000, then simplifying.

| Example 4 | Write these decimals as fractions. Give your answers in their simplest terms. |

a) 0.4

1. The final digit is in the tenths column, so write a fraction using 10 as the denominator.

2. Simplify the fraction.

$$0.4 = \frac{4}{10} = \frac{2}{5}$$
$\div 2$ $\div 2$

b) 0.142

1. The final digit is in the thousandths column, so write a fraction using 1000 as the denominator.

2. Simplify the fraction.

$$0.142 = \frac{142}{1000} = \frac{71}{500}$$
$\div 2$ $\div 2$

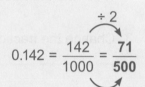

Exercise 2

1 Copy and complete the following:

a) $0.9 = \text{........ tenths} = \frac{9}{\underline{}}$

b) $0.11 = 11 \text{ .... } = \frac{11}{\underline{}}$

c) $0.03 = \text{........ hundredths} = \frac{}{100}$

d) $0.057 = 57 \text{ .... } = \frac{57}{\underline{}}$

2 Write these decimals as fractions without using a calculator.

a) 0.3   b) 0.7   c) 0.01   d) 0.003   e) 0.13   f) 0.017

g) 0.47   h) 0.203   i) 0.063   j) 0.009   k) 0.81   l) 0.01

3 Write these decimals as fractions without using a calculator.
Give your answers in their simplest terms.

a) 0.5   b) 0.8   c) 0.2   d) 0.12   e) 0.44   f) 0.38

g) 0.64   h) 0.04   i) 0.05   j) 0.225   k) 0.045   l) 0.008

Percentages

'Per cent' means 'out of 100'. A <u>percentage</u> is used to write an amount as a number out of 100. It's another way of showing a <u>proportion</u> of something.

Example 5 **This grid is made from 100 small squares.**

a) What percentage of the grid is shaded?

1. Count the number of shaded squares.

   38 squares are shaded.

2. Write this amount as a fraction of the whole grid.

   There are 100 squares, so $\frac{38}{100}$ are shaded.

3. If the denominator is 100, then the numerator is the percentage.

   38% of the grid is shaded.

b) What percentage of the grid is not shaded?

1. You know the percentage that is shaded.

   38% of the grid is shaded.

2. Subtract the percentage that is shaded from the total percentage.

   $100\% - 38\% = \textbf{62\%}$

Exercise 3

Don't use a calculator for this exercise.

1 Each grid is made from 100 squares. Find the percentage of each grid that is:

    i) shaded,   **ii)** not shaded.

a) 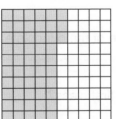   **b)** 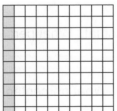   **c)** 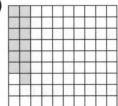   **d)**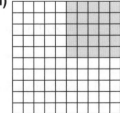

2 A bakery sells 100 loaves of bread. 61 of the loaves are brown and the rest are white.

    a) What percentage of the loaves are brown?

    b) What percentage of the loaves are white?

Example 6	Write each of these amounts as a percentage without using a calculator:

a) 3 out of 10

1. Write the amount as a fraction.
2. Write this as an equivalent fraction over 100.
3. The numerator is the percentage.

$$\frac{3}{10} \overset{\times 10}{=} \frac{30}{100} = \mathbf{30\%}$$

b) 64 out of 200

1. Write the amount as a fraction.
2. Write this as an equivalent fraction over 100.
3. The numerator is the percentage.

$$\frac{64}{200} \overset{\div 2}{=} \frac{32}{100} = \mathbf{32\%}$$

3 Write each of the following as a percentage:

a) 8 out of 10

b) 4 out of 10

c) 7 out of 50

d) 18 out of 50

e) 70 out of 200

f) 16 out of 200

g) 122 out of 200

h) 2 out of 20

i) $\frac{13}{20}$

j) $\frac{8}{25}$

k) $\frac{15}{25}$

l) $\frac{400}{1000}$

4 Jill scored $\frac{36}{50}$ in a test. What is her mark as a percentage?

5 A 200 g bar of chocolate contains 18 g of fat. What percentage of the chocolate is fat?

6 Rob buys 50 stamps. 41 are first class. What percentage are first class?

7 Peter flipped a coin 25 times. The coin landed showing 'heads' 12 times. What percentage of flips landed with 'tails' showing?

To change from a <u>percentage</u> to a <u>decimal</u>, you can divide by 100.
To change from a decimal to a percentage, multiply by 100.

| Example 7 | Write $\frac{21}{35}$ first as a decimal and then as a percentage. |

1. Divide the top number by the bottom number to get a decimal.

$21 \div 35 = \mathbf{0.6}$

2. Then multiply by 100 to give the percentage.

$0.6 \times 100 = \mathbf{60\%}$

Exercise 4

1 Write each of the following decimals as a percentage.

a) 0.12   **b)** 0.37   **c)** 0.94   **d)** 0.61   **e)** 0.03   **f)** 0.09

2 Write these decimals as **i)** percentages, and **ii)** fractions in their simplest form:

a) 0.67   **b)** 0.77   **c)** 0.01   **d)** 0.05   **e)** 0.45   **f)** 0.84

3 Write these fractions as **i)** decimals, and **ii)** percentages:

a) $\frac{49}{100}$ **b)** $\frac{33}{100}$ **c)** $\frac{3}{10}$ **d)** $\frac{9}{10}$ **e)** $\frac{1}{2}$ **f)** $\frac{1}{4}$ **g)** $\frac{3}{5}$

4 Write these fractions as **i)** decimals, and **ii)** percentages:

a) $\frac{18}{40}$ **b)** $\frac{42}{50}$ **c)** $\frac{39}{150}$ **d)** $\frac{48}{60}$ **e)** $\frac{36}{80}$ **f)** $\frac{30}{75}$

5 James sits an exam and gets a mark of $\frac{54}{75}$. What was his percentage mark?

6 325 students attend a school. 195 of the students are girls.
Give the proportion of boys at the school as a decimal.

7 $\frac{18}{20}$ children in a class prefer dogs to cats.
What percentage of the class prefer cats?

Exercise 5

1 Divide by 100 to write these percentages as decimals:

    a) 12%   **b)** 37%   **c)** 80%   **d)** 29%

    e) 41%   **f)** 3%   **g)** 57%   **h)** 92%

    i) 45%   **j)** 19%   **k)** 6%   **l)** 1%

2 Write these percentages as **i)** decimals, and **ii)** fractions in their simplest form:

    a) 39%   **b)** 48%   **c)** 50%   **d)** 13%

    e) 9%   **f)** 60%   **g)** 25%   **h)** 30%

    i) 55%   **j)** 75%   **k)** 5%   **l)** 22%

3 64% of visitors to a museum left a donation.
Write this percentage as a decimal.

4 85% of customers in a cafe ordered soup for lunch.
Write this percentage as a fraction in its simplest form.

5 53% of the people who visited a museum one day were men.
What proportion of the visitors that day were women? Give your answer as a decimal.

6 In a survey, Lien finds out that 28% of people prefer tea. The rest prefer coffee.
What proportion of people prefer coffee?
Give your answer as a fraction in its simplest form.

> ### Investigate — Percentages in Real Life
>
> *Percentages are everywhere — for example, in shops, adverts and in the news.*
>
> **a)** Between now and your next maths lesson, keep a record of everywhere
> you come across percentages and what they're being used for.
>
> **b)** Why do you think percentages are used so much?
>
> **c)** Can you find anywhere where a percentage is being used in a
> misleading way?

Comparing Proportions

If you need to compare some proportions (fractions, decimals or percentages), convert them to the same type of proportion first. It's usually easiest to change everything to a percentage.

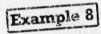 **In a school, 48% of Year 8 are girls.**
90 out of 200 pupils in Year 9 are girls.
Which year has the higher proportion of girls?

1. Change the fraction into a percentage.
$$\frac{90}{200} \overset{\div 2}{\underset{\div 2}{=}} \frac{45}{100} = 45\%$$

2. Compare the two percentages.
48% is bigger than 45%, so **Year 8** has the higher proportion of girls.

Exercise 6

Don't use a calculator for this exercise.

1 Which is bigger:

a) 27% or $\frac{1}{5}$?

b) $\frac{1}{2}$ or 49%?

c) 0.81 or $\frac{4}{5}$?

d) 0.66 or 60%?

2 Write each set of numbers in order, starting with the smallest:

a) 30%, $\frac{28}{100}$, 0.32

b) 0.56, $\frac{1}{2}$, 58%

c) $\frac{1}{5}$, 0.22, 19%

d) $\frac{69}{100}$, 0.7, 71%

e) $\frac{4}{10}$, 0.42, 41%

f) $\frac{2}{5}$, 0.04, 26%

3 a) Write 63% as a decimal.

b) Write $\frac{3}{5}$ as a decimal.

c) Put 63%, $\frac{3}{5}$ and 0.66 in order, from smallest to largest.

4 For each of the following pairs, work out which is larger.

a) 0.44, 40%

b) 0.3, 3%

c) 0.65, 60%

d) 0.08, 80%

e) 0.3, $\frac{29}{100}$

f) 0.1, $\frac{1}{100}$

g) 0.8, $\frac{7}{10}$

h) 0.01, $\frac{2}{20}$

5.5 Percentages of Amounts

Finding Percentages Without a Calculator

Finding a <u>percentage</u> of an amount just means finding a <u>proportion</u> of the total number.

Example 1 Without using a calculator, find 25% of 40.

1. 25% is the same as $\frac{1}{4}$. $\qquad\qquad 25\% = \frac{25}{100} = \frac{1}{4}$

2. So find 25% of 40 by dividing by 4. $\quad 40 \div 4 = \textbf{10}$

Example 2 Find 45% of 80 without a calculator.

1. First find 10% of 80.

   10% is the same as $\frac{1}{10}$, $\qquad 80 \div 10 = 8$
   so divide 80 by 10.

2. Next, find 40% and 5% of 80:
   40% is 10% × 4. $\qquad\qquad 8 \times 4 = 32$
   5% is 10% ÷ 2. $\qquad\qquad 8 \div 2 = 4$

3. Add these two values $\qquad\qquad$ 45% of 80 is 32 + 4 = **36**
   together to find 45%

Exercise 1

Answer these questions **without using a calculator**.

1 Find each of these percentages:

   a) 50% of 8   **b)** 25% of 12   **c)** 50% of 24 cm

   d) 25% of 20 kg   **e)** 50% of £7   **f)** 20% of 30 km

2 **a)** Find 20% of £25.

   b) Use your answer to **a)** to find 80% of £25.

3 50% of a bag of 36 counters are blue. How many counters are blue?

4 Grace gets paid £1200 each month. She saves 25% of everything she gets paid.
How much does she save each month?

5 8000 tickets went on sale for a pantomime. 75% of the tickets were sold to children.
How many tickets were sold to children?

6 Adam counted 160 cars. 25% of them were red.
How many red cars did Adam count?

7 Of the 32 passengers on a train, 75% were adults.
How many adults were on the train?

8 **a)** Find 10% of 60.   **b)** Hence find 20% of 60.

9 **a)** Find 10% of 90.   **b)** Hence find 30% of 90.

10 **a)** Find 10% of 70 kg.   **b)** Hence find 40% of 70 kg.

11 **a)** Find 10% of £30.   **b)** Hence find 60% of £30.

12 Find the value of each of these percentages:

     a) 20% of £120   **b)** 30% of 80p   **c)** 40% of 30 cm   **d)** 70% of 50 miles

13 **a)** Find 10% of 40.   **b)** Hence find 5% of 40.

14 **a)** Find 10% of 160 km.   **b)** Hence find 5% of 160 km.

15 **a)** Find 10% of 60.   **b)** Find 5% of 60.   **c)** Find 15% of 60.

16 **a)** Find 10% of £300.   **b)** Find 5% of £300.   **c)** Find 35% of £300.

17 Chris needs to save £80 for a new camera. He has saved 45% of this amount so far. How much has he saved?

18 Lily buys a pack of charity Christmas cards for £6. 15% of the cost is donated to charity. How much is the donation?

Investigate — Equivalent Percentages

Finding 50% of something is the same as finding one half of it. $50\% = \dfrac{50}{100} = \dfrac{1}{2}$

a) Are there other ways of asking for the same proportion?

b) Start with some different percentages and list as many ways of asking for them as you can.

Finding Percentages Using a Calculator

Example 3 Calculate 87% of £28.

1. Work out what you need to calculate:

   - 87% is the same as $\dfrac{87}{100}$.

   - 'of' means 'multiply'.

   87% of £28 $\longrightarrow \dfrac{87}{100} \times 28$

2. Use a calculator to work this out. $87 \div 100 \times 28 = 24.36$

3. Give your answer with the correct units and number of decimal places.   So, 87% of £28 is **£24.36**

Exercise 2

Use a calculator for this exercise.

1 Copy and complete the working out to find the value of the percentages.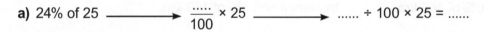

a) 24% of 25 $\longrightarrow \dfrac{\ldots}{100} \times 25 \longrightarrow \ldots \div 100 \times 25 = \ldots$

b) 65% of 180 $\longrightarrow \dfrac{\ldots}{100} \times 180 \longrightarrow \ldots \div 100 \times \ldots = \ldots$

c) 17% of 40 $\longrightarrow \dfrac{\ldots}{100} \times \ldots \longrightarrow \ldots \div 100 \times \ldots = \ldots$

2 Find the value of each of these percentages:

a) 35% of 160

b) 27% of 800

c) 62% of 300

d) 56% of 400

e) 66% of 250

f) 3% of 300

g) 23% of 1500

h) 46% of 390

i) 80% of 58

j) 51% of 620

k) 72% of 28

l) 92% of 45

3 Find the value of each of these percentages:

a) 75% of £15

b) 90% of £8

c) 35% of £21

d) 69% of £70

e) 59% of £24

f) 7% of £150

4 840 students attend a school. 55% of the students are girls.
How many girls attend the school?

5 Anthony spent £88 on a shopping trip. He spent 44% of this on clothes.
How much money did he spend on clothes?

6 A 450 g box of cereal contains raisins and oats. 14% of the weight is raisins.
What is the weight of raisins in the box?

7 Nadia spent £26 on party food. She spent 13% of the money on jelly.
How much did she spend on jelly?

8 Sheila has 75 pairs of socks. 32% of them are green and the rest are blue.
How many pairs are blue?

9 Dom is 67% of the way through a 360 mile journey.
How many miles has he got left to drive? Give your answer to the nearest whole mile.

10 a) Add 27% of 400 to 32% of 50.

b) Subtract 65% of 80 from 96% of 200.

c) Multiply 64% of 25 by 3% of 300.

5.6 Percentage Change

To increase (or decrease) an amount by a percentage:

- first calculate the percentage
- then add this to (or subtract it from) the original amount.

Example 1 **Increase 40 by 20% without using a calculator.**

1. First, work out the percentage. $20\% = \dfrac{1}{5}$, so 20% of 40 is $40 \div 5 = 8$

2. Then add it to the original amount. $40 + 8 = \mathbf{48}$

Example 2 **A shop is offering a 15% discount on all clothes. What is the discounted price of a jacket that normally sells for £45?**

1. Use a calculator to find 15% of the normal selling price. $15 \div 100 \times £45 = £6.75$

2. Subtract this from the normal selling price to find the sale price. $£45 - £6.75 = \mathbf{£38.25}$

Exercise 1

Answer questions 1 to 3 **without using a calculator**.

1 Work out each of the following.

    a) Increase 10 by 50%   **b)** Increase 30 by 50%   **c)** Increase 90 by 10%

    d) Increase 48 by 25%   **e)** Increase £40 by 10%   **f)** Decrease 36 by 50%

    g) Decrease £80 by 25%   **h)** Decrease 70 by 10%   **i)** Decrease £60 by 25%

2 Work out each of the following.

    a) Increase 200 by 20%   **b)** Increase 120 by 75%   **c)** Increase 90 kg by 30%

    d) Increase 350 by 40%   **e)** Decrease 400 by 20%   **f)** Decrease 200 by 30%

    g) Decrease 160 cm by 5%   **h)** Decrease £240 by 20%   **i)** Increase 80 g by 15%

3 Work out each of the following.

a) Increase £40 by 15% b) Decrease 5 cm by 50%

c) Increase £50 by 35% d) Decrease 20 m by 60%

e) Increase 25 mm by 40% f) Increase 60 cm by 30%

g) Decrease £10 by 25% h) Decrease 620 kg by 20%

i) Increase £3.50 by 10% j) Increase 300 km by 45%

Use a calculator for questions 4 and 5.

4 Work out these percentage increases.

a) Increase 125 kg by 24% b) Increase 60 miles by 90%

c) Increase £350 by 22% d) Increase £200 by 18%

e) Increase 96 km by 75% f) Increase $150 by 92%

g) Increase 50 cm by 7% h) Increase 160 kg by 32%

i) Increase £425 by 45% j) Increase 2300 g by 12%

5 Work out these percentage decreases.

a) Decrease 800 kg by 64% b) Decrease 540 m by 75%

c) Decrease £400 by 28% d) Decrease £350 by 6%

e) Decrease £290 by 33% f) Decrease £470 by 63%

g) Decrease 520 mm by 80% h) Decrease £390 by 20%

i) Decrease £64 by 65% j) Decrease 1200 miles by 8%

Answer questions 6 to 11 **without using a calculator**.

6 A bar of chocolate normally weighs 200 g. A special offer means an extra 25% is included in each packet. How much chocolate is in the special offer packet?

7 A restaurant adds a 10% service charge to a customer's bill.
How much does the customer pay in total when the bill is £80 before the service is added?

8 In a sale there is 30% off the cost of all televisions.
What is the sale price of a television normally costing £400?

9 A tennis racquet normally costing £45 is reduced in a sale by 20%.
What is the sale price of the tennis racquet?

10 A museum has 1200 visitors in November. The number of visitors is predicted to decrease by 10% in December. How many visitors are expected in December?

11 Tom put £50 in a savings account. Each year, 5% of the amount in the account is added as interest. How much money is in Tom's account after one year?

Use a calculator to answer questions 12 to 15.

12 The price of a cupcake was 80p.
The price is increased by 35%. What is the new cost of a cupcake?

13 Beth normally gets paid £820 a month. She gets a pay rise of 4%.
How much does she now get paid each month?

14 A pair of jeans that usually costs £43 is reduced in a sale by 25%.
What is the sale price of the jeans?

15 It costs £7.50 for an adult to play mini-golf. It costs 42% less for a child to play mini-golf.
How much does it cost for a child to play mini-golf?

Investigate — Missing Money

a) One week, Ted got a 20% bonus on his £100 a week wages.
How much did he get in total that week?

b) His boss then realised that Ted hadn't deserved his bonus, so he asked him to pay back 20% of what he received. How much is this?

c) How much was Ted left with? How can you explain the missing money?

Section 6 — Ratio and Proportion

6.1 Comparing Quantities

Using Fractions

You can write one number as a <u>fraction</u> of another by putting the first number over the second and <u>cancelling down</u>. If the first number is bigger than the second, you'll end up with a fraction greater than 1.

If you multiply the fraction by the second number, you end up with the first number again.

Example 1

a) **Write 27 as a fraction of 36.**

Put 27 over 36 and cancel down.

$$\frac{27}{36} = \frac{3}{4}$$

with $\div 9$ arrows top and bottom.

b) **What fraction must you multiply 36 by to get 27?**

This is the fraction you've just found.

$\frac{3}{4}$

Check your answer by doing the multiplication: $36 \times \frac{3}{4} = 27$.

Exercise 1

For this exercise, give all fractions in their simplest terms, leaving them as top-heavy fractions where necessary.

1 a) Write 16 as a fraction of 20.   **b)** Write 25 as a fraction of 40.

   c) Write 7 as a fraction of 21.   **d)** Write 32 as a fraction of 64.

2 a) Write 9 as a fraction of 6.   **b)** Write 18 as a fraction of 8.

   c) Write 49 as a fraction of 28.   **d)** Write 38 as a fraction of 24.

3 a) i) Write 22 as a fraction of 32.   **ii)** Write 32 as a fraction of 22.

   b) What fraction must you multiply 32 by to get 22?

4 a) i) Write 45 as a fraction of 54.   **ii)** Write 54 as a fraction of 45.

   b) What fraction must you multiply 45 by to get 54?

5   There are 15 Year 7 students, 12 Year 8 students and 14 Year 9 students on a trip.

   a) Write the number of Year 8 students as a fraction of the number of Year 7 students.

   b) Write the number of Year 9 students as a fraction of the number of Year 8 students.

6   What fraction must you multiply 48 by to get 64?

7   Fill in the gap in the following multiplication: 39 × ☐ = 65

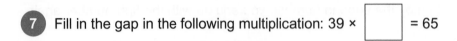

8   The contents of a packet of jelly sweets are shown in this table:

   a) Write the number of orange jelly sweets as a fraction of the total number of jelly sweets in the packet.

   b) Write the number of red jelly sweets as a fraction of the number of pink jelly sweets.

   c) Complete this sentence:

Colour	Number of jelly sweets
Red	7
Yellow	5
Pink	4
Green	6
Orange	11

   The number of ☐ jelly sweets as a fraction

   of the number of ☐ jelly sweets is $\frac{3}{2}$.

Using Percentages

You can write one number as a <u>percentage</u> of another by dividing the first number by the second and multiplying by 100. If the first number is bigger than the second, you'll end up with a percentage greater than 100%.

> **Example 2** In a female choir, there are 8 altos and 10 sopranos.
>
> **a)** **Write the number of altos as a percentage of the number of sopranos.**
>
> Divide the number of altos by the number of sopranos, and multiply by 100.
>
> 8 ÷ 10 = 0.8
> 0.8 × 100 = **80%**
>
> **b)** **Write the number of sopranos as a percentage of the number of altos.**
>
> Divide the number of sopranos by the number of altos, and multiply by 100.
>
> 10 ÷ 8 = 1.25
> 1.25 × 100 = **125%**

Exercise 2

1 **a)** Write 14 as a percentage of 20.

b) Write 24 as a percentage of 80.

c) Write 39 as a percentage of 52.

d) Write 75 as a percentage of 125.

2 **a)** Write 18 as a percentage of 15.

b) Write 92 as a percentage of 80.

c) Write 48 as a percentage of 24.

d) Write 20 as a percentage of 8.

3 On a bookshelf, there are 16 fiction books and 20 non-fiction books.

a) Write the number of fiction books as a percentage of the number of non-fiction books.

b) Write the number of non-fiction books as a percentage of the number of fiction books.

4 In a fruit bowl, there are 10 apples and 25 oranges.

a) Write the number of apples as a percentage of the number of oranges.

b) Write the number of oranges as a percentage of the number of apples.

5 On a pond, there are 26 ducks, 9 swans and 5 geese.

a) Write the number of ducks as a percentage of the total number of birds on the pond.

b) Write the number of swans as a percentage of the number of geese.

c) Write the number of ducks as a percentage of the number of geese.

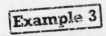 It costs Sam £1.50 to make a birthday card, which she then sells for £2.25.
What is her percentage profit?

1. First, find the profit — this is the difference between the selling price and how much it cost to make.

   £2.25 − £1.50 = £0.75

2. Then write the profit as a percentage of the original amount — divide the profit by the cost to make and multiply by 100.

   £0.75 ÷ £1.50 = 0.5
   0.5 × 100 = **50%**

Exercise 3

1   Paul buys a pair of walking boots for £15 and sells them for £18.

  a) How much profit does he make?

  b) Write the profit as a percentage of the original cost of the walking boots.

2   It costs Lois £10 to make a sculpture. She sells the sculpture for £6.

  a) How much money does she lose?

  b) Write the loss as a percentage of the cost of making the sculpture.

3   It costs Katie £6 to make a cake, which she then sells for £7.50.

  a) How much profit does she make?

  b) Write the profit as a percentage of the cost of making the cake.

4   Russ bought a bike for £400 and sold it a year later for £280.

  a) How much money does he lose?

  b) Write the loss as a percentage of the original cost of the bike.

5   A business makes calendars at a cost of £7 each. It sells the calendars for £10.50.
    What is the percentage profit on each calendar?

6   Conrad buys a garden bench for £40. When it falls apart, he sells the wood for £16.
    What is his percentage loss?

7   Alec buys a car for £6000 and sells it 2 years later for £4800.
    What is his percentage loss?

8   A business makes sandwiches at a cost of 50p each and sells them for £2.
    What is the percentage profit on each sandwich?

Using Ratios

You can use <u>ratios</u> to compare amounts of things.

To write quantities in ratios, you have to translate the information into maths.

So 'twice as many apples as oranges' written as a ratio would be 2:1 (apples:oranges), and 'half as many dogs as cats' would be written 1:2 (dogs:cats).

You can turn a ratio into a <u>fraction</u> by putting one bit of the ratio on top of the other.

Example 4 | **For this triangle, write down the ratio of its height to its base length.**

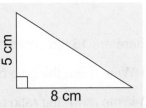

1. The height is 5 cm and the base is 8 cm long.

2. Write out the ratio in words, with the height first.   height:base length

3. Write the numbers in. Check both measurements have the same units.   5 cm:8 cm

4. The units are the same, so take them out to give the final answer.   **5:8**

Example 5 | **A recipe calls for three times as much flour as sugar.**

a) Write the amount of flour compared to the amount of sugar as a ratio.

'Three times' as much flour as sugar means that for every 1 part of sugar, there must be 3 parts of flour. So write this as a ratio.   flour:sugar   = 3:1

b) Write the amount of sugar compared to the amount of flour as a fraction.

Put the numbers from your ratio into a fraction. You want the amount of sugar, so put that part of the ratio on the top of the fraction.   The recipe needs $\frac{1}{3}$ as much sugar as flour.

Exercise 4

1 For each of the following, write down:

   a) the ratio of circles to triangles   **b)** the ratio of triangles to circles

2 Write down:

a) the ratio of hippos to giraffes   **b)** the ratio of giraffes to hippos

3 There are 15 red socks and 19 blue socks in a drawer.

a) Write down the ratio of red socks to blue socks.

b) Write down the ratio of blue socks to red socks.

4 In a cupboard, there are 5 plates and 7 bowls.
Write down the ratio of bowls to plates.

5 A bird is 37 cm long (from beak to tail) and has a wingspan of 81 cm.

a) Write down the ratio of the bird's length to its wingspan.

b) Write down the ratio of its wingspan to its length.

6 For this rectangle, write down the ratio of its longest side to its shortest side.

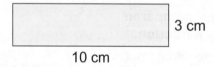

3 cm

10 cm

7 For this triangle, write down the ratio of its shortest side to its longest side.

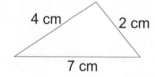

4 cm   2 cm

7 cm

8   A steak pie costs 78p and a cheese and onion pie costs 61p.
Write down the ratio of the cost of a steak pie to the cost of a cheese and onion pie.

9   Nigel and George are both travelling from Paris-upon-Tyne to Rome-by-the-Sea.
Nigel travels by train, and his journey takes 8 hours.
George drives, and his journey takes 9 hours.
Write down the ratio of George's journey time to Nigel's journey time.

10   Write the following statements as ratios of CDs to DVDs:

   a) Lucy has twice as many CDs as DVDs.

   b) Ricky has four times as many DVDs as CDs.

   c) Amir has half as many CDs as DVDs.

   d) Nancy has five times as many DVDs as CDs.

11   Ellie has three times as many stuffed monkeys as stuffed rabbits.

   a) Write down the ratio of stuffed monkeys to stuffed rabbits.

   b) Write down the ratio of stuffed rabbits to stuffed monkeys.

12   Mike has won 13 basketball games, lost 11 and drawn 2.

   a) Write down the ratio of games won to games lost.

   b) Write down the ratio of games lost to games drawn.

   c) Write down the ratio of games won to games lost to games drawn.

13   A bakery sells only white and wholemeal loaves of bread.
The ratio of white loaves to wholemeal loaves sold is 5:2.

   a) Write the number of wholemeal loaves sold as a fraction
   of the number of white loaves sold.

   b) Write the number of white loaves sold as a fraction
   of the number of wholemeal loaves sold.

   c) Write the number of white loaves sold as a fraction
   of the total number of loaves sold.

14 A choir has 6 times as many female members as male members.

  a) Write the number of female to male members as a ratio.

  b) Complete the statement: There are ☐ times as many male members as female members.

15 Harry is given a box of toy lorries and cars. $\frac{4}{5}$ of the vehicles in the box are lorries.

  a) What fraction of the vehicles are cars?

  b) Write down the ratio of lorries to cars.

  c) Write the number of cars as a fraction of the number of lorries.

16 Neil has four times as many sheep as cows on his farm, and half as many goats as sheep. Write this information as a ratio. Give your answer in the form sheep : cows : goats.

17 The ratio of Irish Setters to Labradors to Great Danes in a class at a dog show is 3 : 4 : 1. All the dogs in the class are either Irish Setters, Labradors or Great Danes.

  a) Write the number of Irish Setters as a fraction of the number of Labradors.

  b) Write the number of Irish Setters as a percentage of the number of Great Danes.

  c) Write the number of Labradors as a fraction of the total number of dogs in the class.

Investigate — Paper Ratios

  a) A piece of A4 paper has a width of 210 mm and a height of 297 mm. Write down the ratio of the width to the height.

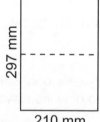

  b) Find the width as a fraction of the height using a calculator.

  c) A5 paper can be made by cutting the A4 paper in half, as shown by the dotted line. Work out the width and height of the A5 paper, and write it as a ratio and fraction as you did for parts **a)** and **b)**.

  d) A6, A7 and A8 paper are all made by halving the previous size. Work out the ratios and fractions of their widths and heights as before. What do you notice about the ratios and fractions each time?

6.2 Ratio and Proportion

Simplifying Ratios

You can <u>simplify</u> ratios by dividing the numbers by a <u>common factor</u>.

> **Example 1**   **Write the ratio 16 : 40 in its simplest form.**
>
> 1. Look for a number that divides into both 16 and 40.   8 divides into 16 and 40
>
> 2. Divide both sides of the ratio by this number. $16 \div 8 = 2$ and $40 \div 8 = 5$
>
> 3. Make sure no other numbers divide into both sides of the ratio — that means it's in its simplest form.   So the ratio can be written as **2 : 5**, which is the simplest form.

Exercise 1

1   Write each of the following ratios in its simplest form.

     a) 4 : 8   **b)** 3 : 6   **c)** 6 : 18   **d)** 5 : 20

     e) 12 : 3   **f)** 16 : 8   **g)** 21 : 7   **h)** 24 : 12

     i) 4 : 6   **j)** 15 : 25   **k)** 12 : 30   **l)** 22 : 55

     m) 20 : 16   **n)** 27 : 18   **o)** 45 : 30   **p)** 42 : 28

2   Write down the ratio of squares to circles.
    Give your answer in its simplest form.

3   Write down the ratio of big squares to little squares.
    Give your answer in its simplest form.

4 A necklace is made up of 15 gold beads, 27 silver beads and 35 blue beads.
Find the following ratios. Give your answers in their simplest form.

   a) The ratio of gold beads to silver beads.

   b) The ratio of gold beads to blue beads.

5 On a school bus, there are 24 girls and 36 boys.
What is the ratio of girls to boys?
Give your answer in its simplest form.

6 A salad dressing is made by mixing 15 tablespoons of olive oil
with 6 tablespoons of balsamic vinegar.
Find the ratio of oil to vinegar in its simplest form.

Finding Amounts Using Ratios

You can use ratios to solve problems.
You can scale up a ratio by multiplying each side of the ratio by the same number.

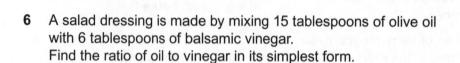

Example 2	The ratio of apples to oranges on a fruit stall is $5:3$. If there are 30 apples on the stall, how many oranges are there?

1. Work out what you need to multiply by   apples : oranges
to go from 5 to 30 on the left-hand side.
$30 ÷ 5 = 6$, so multiply by 6.

$$×6 \left(\begin{array}{c} 5:3 \\ 30:18 \end{array} \right) ×6$$

2. Multiply the right-hand side by the same   So there are **18 oranges**.
number to find the number of oranges.

Exercise 2

1 At a pet shop, the ratio of hamsters to guinea pigs is $5:2$.
If there are 20 hamsters, how many guinea pigs are there?

2 In a class, the ratio of left-handed people to right-handed people is $2:9$.
If there are 6 left-handed people in the class, how many right-handed people are there?

3   Georgia is sharing sweets with her brother in the ratio 3:5.
If her brother gets 25 sweets, how many sweets does Georgia get?

4   In a garden, for every 4 rose bushes there are 7 azaleas.
If there are 21 azaleas, how many rose bushes are there?

For questions **5-9**, remember to give the correct units in your answer.

5   Purple paint is made by mixing blue paint and red paint in the ratio 2:3.
If 4 litres of blue paint are used, how much red paint is needed?

6   In a recipe, flour and butter are used in the ratio 3:1.
If 600 g of flour are used, how much butter is needed?

7   Ed and Jo share some money in the ratio 7:3. If Ed gets £21, how much does Jo get?

8   The ratio of Tom's height to Lisa's height is 8:5. If Tom is 168 cm tall, how tall is Lisa?

9   Milly and Lotte are knitting scarves. For every 6 cm that Milly knits, Lotte knits 11 cm.
If Milly knits a scarf that is 1.2 m long, how long will Lotte's scarf be in metres?

You can use ratios to <u>divide</u> an amount into two or more shares. Use the total number
of parts to find the size of one part, then use this to find the size of each share.

Example 3 Divide £40 in the ratio 2:3.	
1. Add up the numbers in the ratio to find the total number of parts.	2 + 3 = 5 parts altogether
2. Work out the amount for one part.	5 parts = £40, so 1 part = £40 ÷ 5 = **£8**
3. Then multiply the amount for one part by the number of parts for each share. (To check, if you add up the shares, you should get the original amount.)	£8 × 2 = £16 £8 × 3 = £24 So the shares are **£16** and **£24** (and £16 + £24 = £40).

Exercise 3

1 **a)** Divide 16 in the ratio 1:3. **b)** Divide 21 in the ratio 3:4.

2 **a)** Divide 33 in the ratio 3:8. **b)** Divide 39 in the ratio 6:7.

3 Divide £30 in the following ratios:

   a) 1:5 **b)** 2:3 **c)** 3:7 **d)** 7:8

4 Share 64 kg in the following ratios:

   a) 1:3 **b)** 1:7 **c)** 5:11 **d)** 15:17

5 Find the larger amount when each amount below is divided into the given ratio.

   a) 120 ml in the ratio 7:13 **b)** 75 mm in the ratio 11:14

   c) £150 in the ratio 12:13 **d)** 420 g in the ratio 4:17

6 In a school of 500 pupils, the ratio of pupils who wear glasses to pupils who don't wear glasses is 33:67. How many pupils don't wear glasses?

7 Justin is 7 and Lee is 18. They share £2000 in the ratio of their ages. How much does each person get?

> ### Investigate — Proportion
>
>   A toy-making robot can make 20 toys in an hour.
>
> **a)** How many toys could 2 robots make in an hour? How many toys could 3 robots make in an hour? How many toys could 1000 robots make in an hour?
>
> **b)** How long would it take 2 robots to make 20 toys? How long would it take 5 robots to make 20 toys? How long would it take 10 robots to make 20 toys?
>
> **c)** What do you notice about the different calculations you have to make for parts **a)** and **b)**? Can you explain why they're different?

Section 7 — Units and Scales

7.1 Time

Clock Time

Times can be given in the 12-hour clock or the 24-hour clock.

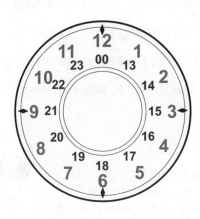

Starting at midnight, the first time
round the clock runs from...

24-hour clock	12-hour clock
00:00	12 midnight
to	to
11:59	11:59 am

and the second time round runs from...

24-hour clock	12-hour clock
12:00	12 noon
to	to
23:59	11:59 pm

12-hour clock times need 'am' or 'pm' to show if the time is before or after noon.
24-hour clock times always have four digits, e.g. 02:30.

For times from 1:00 pm, add 12 hours to the 12-hour clock time to get the 24-hour clock
time (or subtract 12 hours from the 24-hour clock time to get the 12-hour clock time).

Example 1

a) Write 8:30 pm using 24-hour clock time.

This time is after 1:00 pm, so add
12 hours to the 12-hour clock time.

$8:30 + 12:00 = \mathbf{20:30}$
in 24-hour clock

b) Write 18:10 using 12-hour clock time.

1. This time is after 13:00, so subtract 12 hours
from the 24-hour clock time.

2. It needs a 'pm' to show that it's after noon.

$18:10 - 12:00 = \mathbf{6:10\ pm}$
in 12-hour clock

Exercise 1

1   Write these 12-hour clock times as 24-hour clock times.

a) 7:35 am   b) 12:15 pm   c) 3:20 am   d) 2:40 pm

e) 11:50 am   f) 10:25 pm   g) 12:11 am   h) 5:48 pm

2 Write these 24-hour clock times as 12-hour clock times.

a) 09:50   b) 15:20   c) 04:15   d) 12:18

e) 11:25   f) 19:40   g) 00:45   h) 22:42

3 Write each of these times using: **i)** the 12-hour clock   **ii)** the 24-hour clock

a) 4 o'clock in the afternoon   b) Half past eight in the morning

c) Ten past eleven in the evening   d) Quarter past six in the morning

e) Quarter to three in the afternoon   f) Twenty-five to seven in the evening

Units of Time

The standard units of time are <u>hours</u>, <u>minutes</u> and <u>seconds</u>.
There are 60 seconds in a minute and 60 minutes in an hour.
You can use these facts to convert between hours, minutes and seconds.

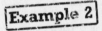 **Peter cycles for 3 hours and 20 minutes.**
What is this time in minutes?

1. First, change 3 hours into minutes   1 hour = 60 minutes, so
   by multiplying by 60.   3 hours = 3 × 60 = 180 minutes

2. Then add on the remaining 20 minutes
   to find the total time in minutes.   180 + 20 = **200 minutes**

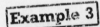 **A music video lasts for 165 seconds.**
What is this in minutes and seconds?

1. Change 165 seconds into   1 minute = 60 seconds, so
   minutes by dividing by 60.   165 seconds = 165 ÷ 60 = 2.75 minutes

2. So 165 seconds is 2 whole
   minutes plus 0.75 of a minute.

3. Find 0.75 of a minute in
   seconds by multiplying by 60.   0.75 × 60 = 45 seconds

4. Finally, put the whole minutes
   and the seconds together.   165 seconds = **2 minutes and 45 seconds**

Exercise 2

1 Rewrite these times in minutes:

a) 2 hours   b) 6 hours   c) 4 hours and 30 minutes   d) 5 hours and 25 minutes

2 Rewrite these times in seconds:

    a) 5 minutes   **b)** 8 minutes   **c)** 15 minutes

    d) 11 minutes   **e)** 3 minutes and 15 seconds   **f)** 4 minutes and 10 seconds

3 Rewrite these times in hours and minutes:

    a) 180 minutes   **b)** 150 minutes   **c)** 225 minutes   **d)** 247 minutes

4 Rewrite these times in minutes and seconds:

    a) 300 seconds   **b)** 90 seconds   **c)** 136 seconds   **d)** 199 seconds

5 Rewrite these times in hours:

    a) 330 minutes   **b)** 105 minutes   **c)** 3 hours and 12 minutes

6   **a)** Write 0.5 hours in minutes

    b) Use your answer to part **a)** to write 3.5 hours in minutes.

7 A song lasts for 3.25 minutes. What is this time in seconds?

8   **a)** Write 1.5 hours in minutes.

    b) Use your answer to part **a)** to write 1.5 hours in seconds.

> ### Investigate — Time
>
> Imagine a new world, where there are 100 seconds
> in a new-minute, and 100 new-minutes in a new-hour.
>
> **a)** Would a new-minute be longer or shorter than one of our minutes?
>
> **b)** How many seconds would be in a new-hour?
> How many new-minutes long would your maths lesson be?
>
> **c)** Design a clock for the new world.
> How many new-hours do you think there would be in a new-day?

Calculations with Time

| Example 4 | Caitlin starts to watch a film at 7:30 pm. The film lasts for 1 hour and 45 minutes. What time will it finish? |

1. First add on the hours.   7:30 pm + 1 hour = 8:30 pm

2. Then add on the minutes.   8:30 pm + 45 minutes = **9:15 pm**

| Example 5 | Scott's train departs at 09:35 and arrives at 11:25. How long is the journey? |

1. Split the journey into short easy stages, and find the time taken for each stage.

      09:35 ⟶ 10:00 ⟶ 11:00 ⟶ 11:25
          25 minutes   1 hour   25 minutes

2. Add the times for each stage together to find the total journey time.

     25 minutes + 1 hour + 25 minutes = **1 hour and 50 minutes**

Exercise 3

1   During a workout, Nikolai jogs for 30 minutes, rows for 20 minutes and lifts weights for 15 minutes. How long is his workout?

2   Find the arrival time for each journey below:

    a) Start time = 8:15 am, length of journey = 55 minutes

    b) Start time = 12:50 pm, length of journey = 1 hour and 20 minutes

    c) Start time = 17:24, length of journey = 37 minutes

    d) Start time = 14:40, length of journey = 2 hours and 28 minutes

3   Josie sets off for school at 08:07. Her journey takes 37 minutes. What time will she arrive at school?

4   Marco runs a half-marathon in 2 hours and 25 minutes. He starts running at 09:45. What time does he finish?

5   Robert leaves work at 5:45 pm. His journey home usually takes 35 minutes, but roadworks delay him by 15 minutes. What time will he arrive home?

6 Find the length of each journey below:

    a) Start time = 10:40 am, end time = 11:25 am

    b) Start time = 13:15, end time = 13:50

    c) Start time = 20:45, end time = 22:10

    d) Start time = 9:25 am, end time = 1:15 pm

7 A film starts at 7:45 pm and finishes at 10:05 pm. How long is the film?

8 Rebecca started painting her bathroom at 11:45.
She stopped painting at 16:05. How long was she painting for?

9 A group of scouts have been on a hike that took them 6 hours and 17 minutes.
They finish at 5:15 pm. What time did they start the hike?

10 Connor has a DVD that lasts for 2 hours and 10 minutes.
What is the latest time he can start watching it if he needs to finish by 20:15?

Timetables

Timetables usually show times written in 24-hour clock time.
You can use them to help you plan a journey.

Example 6			

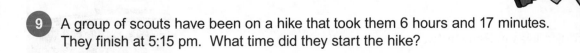

Northpost	0803	0848	0921
Eastwick	0815	0900	0933
Southdale	0827	0912	0945
Westfield	0835	0920	0953

    a) A bus leaves Eastwick at 09:00. What time does it arrive in Westfield?

    1. Find the row for Eastwick and read across until you get to 09:00.

    2. Follow the column down until you get to the row for Westfield.   **09:20**

    **b) Freddie needs to be in Southdale before 9:30 am.
    What's the latest time he can leave Northpost?**

    1. Look at the row for Southdale — there are 2 buses that arrive before 9:30 am.   The buses arrive in Southdale at 08:27 and 09:12.

    2. Follow the columns up until you find the time each bus leaves Northpost.   The latest time he can leave Northpost is **08:48**.

Exercise 4

Use this bus timetable to answer all the questions in this exercise.

Lythington	0530	0645	0810	0920	1015
Greenpool	0632	0747	0912	1022	1117
Penworthy	0651	0806	0931	1042	1136
Underwood	0728	0843	1008	1119	1213
Islingham	0806	0921	1046	1157	1251
Towervale	0858	1013	1138	1249	1343

1   **a)** What time does the earliest bus for Islingham leave Greenpool?

   b) What time does this bus arrive in Islingham?

   c) How long does this journey take?

2   Louisa lives in Penworthy.

   a) What time is the latest bus she can catch to Towervale?

   b) What time does this bus arrive in Towervale?

   c) Give the departure and arrival times of this bus in 12-hour clock time.

3   Joe catches the 06:45 bus from Lythington to Greenpool each day.

   a) What time does he arrive in Greenpool?

   b) How long does this journey take?

   c) One day, the bus is running 15 minutes late. What time will Joe arrive in Greenpool if the journey time is the same as usual?

4   Will lives 10 minutes away from the bus stop in Underwood.
   He needs to be in Towervale by 12 noon. What is the latest time he can leave his house?

5   Diane lives in Greenpool and starts work in Underwood at 9 am.
   It takes two minutes to walk from the bus stop in Underwood to where she works.

   a) What is the latest bus she can catch to make it to work on time?

   b) Some roadworks mean that the bus journey takes 12 minutes longer than usual.
   If Diane catches the bus from part **a)**, will she arrive at work on time?

Speed

Speed is how fast an object is travelling. It's worked out by dividing the distance the object travels by the time it takes.

Speed, distance and time are connected by the formula: $\text{Speed} = \dfrac{\text{Distance}}{\text{Time}}$

Speed units (e.g. km/h) are a combination of the distance units (e.g. km) and time units (e.g. hours).

Example 7 **Graham cycles 30 km in 2 hours.**
What is his average speed?

1. Write down the formula for speed.

2. Put your numbers for distance and time into the formula.

3. Give your answer in the correct units — the distance is in km and the time is in hours, so the speed will be in km per hour (km/h).

$\text{Speed} = \dfrac{\text{Distance}}{\text{Time}}$

$= \dfrac{30}{2} = 30 \div 2$

$= \textbf{15 km/h}$

Exercise 5

1 Find the average speed in km/h of each of these journeys:

   a) distance = 15 km, time = 3 hours

   b) distance = 20 km, time = 5 hours

   c) distance = 40 km, time = 8 hours

   d) distance = 90 km, time = 3 hours

   e) distance = 120 km, time = 6 hours

   f) distance = 5000 km, time = 10 hours

2 A car travels 180 miles in 3 hours.
     Find its average speed in miles per hour (mph).

3 A dog runs 125 m in 25 seconds.
     Find its average speed in metres per second (m/s).

4   A plane flies 2000 miles in 4 hours.
Find its average speed in miles per hour (mph).

5   Find the speed of the following.
Give your answer using the units given in each question.

a) a man running 16 km in 2 hours

b) a lorry travelling 140 miles in 4 hours

c) a bird flying 500 m in 80 seconds

d) a cyclist travelling 48 km in 5 hours

e) a skier travelling 700 m in 140 seconds

f) a snail crawling 1 m in 40 seconds

6   A car travels 18 km in 30 minutes.

a) Convert 30 minutes into hours.

b) Find the average speed of the car in km/h.

7   A rocket travels 4250 miles in 15 minutes.

a) Convert 15 minutes into hours.

b) Find the average speed of the rocket in miles per hour (mph).

8   Find the speed for each of the following journeys.
Give your answers in the units stated.

a) Distance = 315 miles, time = 4 and a half hours, speed = mph

b) Distance = 27 km, time = 45 minutes, speed = km/h

c) Distance = 11 000 m, time 2 hours, speed = km/h

d) Distance = 2000 km, time = 2 hours and 30 minutes, speed = km/h

e) Distance = 2500 m, time = 30 minutes, speed = km/h

f) Distance = 8.5 miles, time = half an hour, speed = mph

7.2 Money

Calculations with Money

The standard units of money in the UK are pounds (£) and pence (p).

£1 = 100p and 1p = £0.01

The different coins used are 1p, 2p, 5p, 10p, 20p, 50p, £1 and £2, and there are £5, £10, £20 and £50 notes as well. Any amount of money can be made from different combinations of these coins and notes — for example, £36 could be made from a £20 note, a £10 note, a £5 note and a £1 coin (there are other ways to make this amount).

Other currencies are worth different amounts but they work in a similar way — there are 100 cents in a euro (€) and 100 cents in an American dollar ($).
To convert between different currencies, you need to know the exchange rate.

Example 1 Aaron has been saving 1p, 2p and 5p coins.
He has 176 pennies, 92 2p coins and 48 5p coins.
Work out the smallest number of notes and coins
he could change these for at the bank.

1. First, work out how much money he has in total (in £).

   176 1p coins = 176p
   92 2p coins = 92 × 2 = 184p
   48 5p coins = 48 × 5 = 240p

2. Then work out how to make this amount using the smallest number of coins and notes.

   Total = 176p + 184p + 240p = 600p = £6

   £6 = £5 + £1
       = **one £5 note and one £1 coin**

Example 2 A bank offers an exchange rate from pounds to euros
of £1 = €1.10.

a) **Mia wants to change some money into euros at the bank.
How many euros will she get for £150?**

£1 is worth €1.10, so multiply the amount she wants to change by the exchange rate.

£150 × 1.10 = **€165**

b) **After her holiday, she has €22 left. How many pounds can
she exchange her euros for at the same exchange rate?**

1. Using the exchange rate, work out how much €1 is worth.

   €1.10 = £1,
   so €1 = £1 ÷ 1.10 = £0.909...

2. Then multiply by the number of euros Mia has.

   €22 = 22 × £0.909... = **£20**

Exercise 1

1 Find the total amount of money for each set of coins and notes.

   a) One £20 note, two £10 notes, four £1 coins and one 50p coin

   b) Three £10 notes, one £5 note, four £2 coins, three 20p coins and one 5p coin

   c) Four £5 notes, three £1 coins, one 50p coin, three 20p coins and two 5p coins

   d) Two £20 notes, three £5 notes, six £2 coins, five 50p coins and eight 2p coins

2 Kelly is going on holiday to Italy. She has one €100 note, five €50 notes, four €20 notes, four €10 notes and eight €5 notes. How much money does she have in total?

3 Find the smallest number of coins and notes you could use to make each amount. Give the value of the coins and notes you use.

   a) £7   **b)** £16   **c)** £28   **d)** £12.50

   e) £21.30   **f)** £32.25   **g)** £2.18   **h)** £11.84

4 Molly's grandma gives her a jar of coins.
   In the jar, there are 206 1p coins, 112 2p coins and 46 5p coins.

   a) How much money is there in the jar? Give your answer in pounds.

   b) Find the smallest number of coins and notes she could exchange this for at the bank.

5 Convert the following amounts into dollars ($) if £1 is worth $1.50.

   a) £10   **b)** £200   **c)** £120   **d)** £80

   e) £75   **f)** £165   **g)** £295   **h)** £32.50

6 Convert the following amounts into euros (€) if £1 is worth €1.20.

   a) £20   **b)** £500   **c)** £350   **d)** £60

   e) £45   **f)** £195   **g)** £235   **h)** £22.50

7 Convert the following amounts into euros (€) if £20 is worth €23.

   a) £50   **b)** £180   **c)** £1500   **d)** £725

8 At the end of his holiday, Bradley had $62 left. He changed the money back into pounds using the exchange rate £1 = $1.55. How many pounds did he get back?

9 Using an exchange rate of £1 = €1.16, convert €580 into pounds.

10 Using an exchange rate of £100 = $160, change $800 into pounds.

> **Investigate — Small Change**
>
> Imagine you have one each of the following coins: 1p, 2p, 5p, 10p and 20p.
>
> **a)** What is the biggest amount you can make using these coins?
>
> **b)** Which other amounts can you make? Which ones can't you make?
>
> **c)** Repeat steps **a)** and **b)**, but this time imagine you have one each of a 1p, 2p, 4p, 8p and 16p coin. Do you get different results?

Unit Pricing

To compare prices and find the 'best buy', you have to look at <u>unit pricing</u>. This means dividing to find the price per unit (e.g. per item, per gram, per litre) or amount per penny (e.g. grams per penny).

Example 3   **6 cakes cost £15. Find the cost of 10 cakes.**

1. Find the cost of one cake by dividing the total cost by the number of cakes.
   6 cakes cost £15 so 1 cake costs £15 ÷ 6 = £2.50

2. Then multiply by the new number of cakes.
   10 cakes cost 10 × £2.50 = **£25**

Exercise 2

1 1 pizza costs £8. Find the cost of:

    a) 3 pizzas   **b)** 7 pizzas   **c)** 15 pizzas

2 6 cupcakes cost £9.

    a) Find the cost of 1 cupcake.

    b) Use your answer to part **a)** to find the cost of 20 cupcakes.

3 4 candles cost £3.60. Find the cost of:

    a) 1 candle   **b)** 8 candles   **c)** 25 candles

4 5 kg of compost costs £7.50. Find the cost of:

    a) 10 kg of compost   **b)** 3 kg of compost   **c)** 100 kg of compost

5 The cost of 8 CDs is £48. What is the cost of 11 CDs if they are all the same price?

6 2 litres of lemonade costs £2.60. Find the cost of 5 litres of lemonade.

Example 4   **A 400 g bag of sweets costs £3.20. A 500 g bag of sweets costs £3.75. Which bag of sweets is the better value?**

1. Find the cost of 1 g of sweets for each bag. It's easier to convert the prices to pence first.

    400 g of sweets costs £3.20,
    so 1 g costs 320p ÷ 400 = 0.8p

    500 g of sweets costs £3.75,
    so 1 g costs 375p ÷ 500 = 0.75p

2. The bag with the lowest cost per gram is the better value.

    The **500 g bag** is the better value.

---

7 A small box contains 5 pencils and costs £3.25.
A large box contains 12 pencils and costs £7.20.

    a) What is the cost of one pencil in the small box?

    b) What is the cost of one pencil in the large box?

    c) Which box is the better value?

8 A small bottle of vinegar contains 400 ml and costs £6.
A large bottle of vinegar contains 600 ml and costs £9.60.

    a) What is the cost in pence of 1 ml of vinegar from the small bottle?

    b) What is the cost in pence of 1 ml of vinegar from the large bottle?

    c) Which bottle is the better value?

9 A bag of 8 apples costs £2.80. A bag of 12 apples costs £3.60.
Which bag is the better value?

10 A 200 g bag of cotton wool costs £1.60. A 500 g bag of cotton wool costs £3.
Which bag is the better value?

11 1.5 m of ribbon costs £1.35. 2 m of the same ribbon costs £1.90.
Which length offers better value for money?

12 The prices to hire a rowing boat for different lengths of time are:

> £8 for 20 minutes
> £10.50 for 40 minutes
> £15 for 1 hour

How long should you hire a rowing boat for to get the best value for money?

Example 5   **A cheese costs £1.25 per 100 g.**
How much cheese can I buy for £10?

1. Find the amount of cheese you can
   buy for £1 by dividing the amount in g
   by the total cost.

   £1.25 buys 100 g of cheese, so
   £1 buys 100 g ÷ £1.25 = 80 g

2. Then multiply by the new amount of money.   £10 buys 80 g × 10 = **800 g**

---

13 15 biscuits cost £3.

a) How many biscuits can be bought for £1?

b) How many biscuits can be bought for £2.20?

14 2.5 kg of rice can be bought for £2. How much rice can be bought for £5?

15 Linda can drive 315 miles on £35 of petrol. How far can she drive on £17 of petrol?

16 After cleaning 12 cars, Ash gets paid £30.
How many cars will he have to clean to reach his target of £80?

7.3 Units and Measuring

Reading Scales

Scales are used to measure things in a particular <u>unit</u> — for example, cm, kg, ml, etc.

Some marks on a scale have a number written next to them. The marks in between are usually left blank — you have to work out what they show.

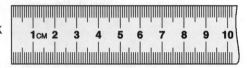

Example 1 | **Find the length of this finger.**

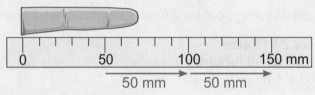

1. The difference between each of the numbered marks on the scale is 50 mm.

2. Each 50 mm gap is divided into 5 smaller intervals, so divide 50 mm by 5 to find what each small division represents.
   $50 \div 5 = 10$, so each small division is 10 mm

3. The length of the finger is 50 mm plus 2 of the small divisions.
   $50 + (2 \times 10) = 70$
   So the finger is **70 mm** long

Exercise 1

1 Find the length of each of these fish. Give your answers in cm.

a)

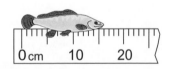

b)

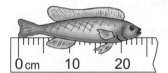

c)

2 a) Write down the difference between each numbered mark on the ruler shown.

b) Find what each small division on the ruler represents.

c) Find the length of the model plane.

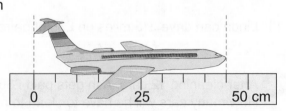

3   Write down the lengths shown by the arrows on the rulers.
Give your answers using the units shown on each ruler.

a)

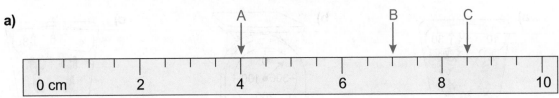

b)

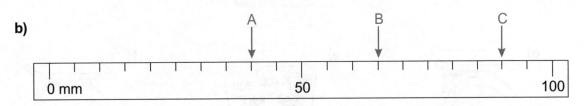

c)

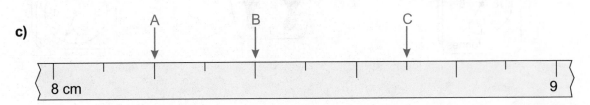

4   Write down the volume of liquid shown in each of these containers.
Give your answers using the units written on each container.

a)

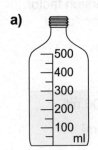

b)

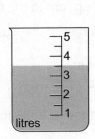

c)

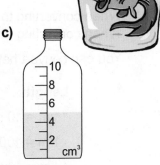

d)

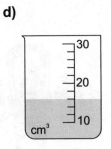

e)

f)

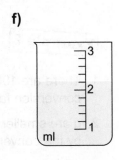

5 Write down the mass shown by the arrow on each of these scales.
Give your answers using the units written on each set of scales.

a)

b)

c)

d)

e)

f)

Metric Units

To convert between different units, you need to know the <u>conversion factor</u>.
This tells you how many times bigger or smaller one unit is than another.

When converting to a smaller unit (e.g. m to cm), multiply by the conversion factor.
When converting to a bigger unit (e.g. cm to m), divide by the conversion factor.

You can convert between different <u>metric units</u> using these conversions:

Length:
1 cm = 10 mm
1 m = 100 cm
1 km = 1000 m

Mass:
1 kg = 1000 g
1 tonne = 1000 kg

Volume:
1 litre (l) = 1000 ml
1 ml = 1 cm³

Example 2   Convert 5 kg into g.

1. There are 1000 g in 1 kg, so the conversion factor is 1000.

   1 kg = 1000 g

2. g are smaller than kg, so multiply by the conversion factor.

   5 kg = (5 × 1000) g
   = **5000 g**

| Example 3 | Convert 145 cm into m. |

1. There are 100 cm in 1 m, so the conversion factor is 100.

   $1 \text{ m} = 100 \text{ cm}$

2. m are bigger than cm, so divide by the conversion factor.

   $145 \text{ cm} = (145 \div 100) \text{ m}$
   $= \textbf{1.45 m}$

Exercise 2

For questions **1-5**, convert each measurement into the units given.

1 **a)** 6 cm into mm

   b) 3 tonnes into kg

   c) 4 litres into ml

   d) 9 m into cm

   e) 12 kg into g

   f) 15 km into m

   g) 120 ml into cm³

   h) 14 cm into mm

2 **a)** 5.7 kg into g

   b) 2.5 cm into mm

   c) 1.6 km into m

   d) 11.2 m into cm

   e) 8.3 litres into ml

   f) 4.9 kg into g

   g) 3.6 ml into cm³

   h) 0.8 tonnes into kg

3 **a)** 700 cm into m

   b) 50 cm³ into ml

   c) 120 mm into cm

   d) 2000 kg into tonnes

   e) 6000 ml into litres

   f) 10 000 m into km

   g) 1400 cm into m

   h) 19 000 ml into litres

4 **a)** 58 mm into cm

   b) 4500 g into kg

   c) 3200 ml into litres

   d) 580 cm into m

   e) 11 400 kg into tonnes

   f) 7800 m into km

   g) 965 mm into cm

   h) 900 g into kg

5 **a)** 28 mm into cm

c) 600 ml into litres

e) 1.7 m into cm

g) 27.8 ml into cm³

b) 4700 g into kg

d) 2400 m into km

f) 30.5 litres into ml

h) 11.7 cm into mm

6 A pencil is 13 cm long. What is its length in mm?

7 A recipe needs 1.2 kg of flour. What is this in g?

8 A bottle contains 400 ml of squash. What is this in litres?

9 An elephant weighs 6800 kg. What is this in tonnes?

10 Jessica runs round a 400 m running track 4 times.
How far has she run in km?

11 A potato weighs 200 g. Brian has 7 potatoes of the same weight.
What is the total weight of the 7 potatoes in kg?

12 Ross is 124 cm tall. Find his height:

a) in mm

b) in m

13 Poppy has made 3.5 litres of tea. She serves it in tea cups that hold 175 ml.

a) Convert 3.5 litres into ml.

b) How many tea cups can she fill?

14 **a)** Convert 0.3 tonnes into kg.

b) Use your answer to part **a)** to convert 0.3 tonnes into g.

Imperial Units

Imperial units are things like inches, feet and yards for length, pounds and ounces for mass and pints and gallons for volume.

You can convert between different imperial units using these conversions:

Length:

1 foot = 12 inches

1 yard = 3 feet

Mass:

1 pound = 16 ounces

1 stone = 14 pounds

Volume:

1 gallon = 8 pints

Example 4 **Convert:**

a) 3 gallons into pints

1. There are 8 pints in 1 gallon, so the conversion factor is 8.

    1 gallon = 8 pints

2. Pints are smaller than gallons, so multiply by the conversion factor.

    3 gallons = (3 × 8) pints
    = **24 pints**

b) 32 pounds into stones and pounds

1. The conversion factor is 14, and stones are bigger than pounds, so divide by 14. Give your answer with a remainder.

    1 stone = 14 pounds

    32 pounds = (32 ÷ 14) stone
    = (2 remainder 4) stone

2. The bit before the remainder is the number of stones, and the remainder is the number of pounds.

    So 32 pounds = **2 stone 4 pounds**

Exercise 3

1 For each of these conversions, write down **i)** the conversion factor, and **ii)** whether you should multiply or divide by the conversion factor.

a) feet into yards

b) pounds into ounces

c) pints into gallons

d) feet into inches

e) pounds into stones

f) inches into feet

For questions **2-5**, convert each measurement into the units given.

2 **a)** 4 feet into inches   **b)** 3 stone into pounds

    c) 5 gallons into pints   **d)** 2 pounds into ounces

    e) 12 yards into feet   **f)** 0.5 stone into pounds

3 **a)** 36 inches into feet   **b)** 80 pints into gallons

    c) 28 pounds into stone   **d)** 21 feet into yards

    e) 40 ounces into pounds   **f)** 30 pints into gallons

4 **a)** 27 feet into yards   **b)** 3.5 pounds into ounces

    c) 120 pints into gallons   **d)** 160 ounces into pounds

5 **a)** 18 inches into feet and inches

    b) 104 pounds into stones and pounds

6 Joshua is 56 inches tall. What is his height in feet and inches?

7 Caitlin has made 5 gallons of fruit punch for a village gala. If the punch is served in half-pint glasses, how many glasses of punch can she serve?

Investigate — Imperial Units

The metric system was introduced in the UK in the late 1960s, but even today we still use imperial units for some measurements.

a) Write a list of as many imperial units you can think of. Next to each one, say where you come across them in the real world.

b) Why do you think we still use imperial units? How are they better than metric units?

7.4 Maps and Scale Drawings

Scales with Units

Maps and plans always have a scale on them.

For example, a map scale of 1 cm : 100 m means that 1 cm on the map represents an actual distance of 100 m.

Example 1 The scale on a map is 1 cm : 5 km.

a) **Two towns are 3 cm apart on the map.**
   How far apart are they in real life?

   Multiply both sides of the scale by   1 cm represents 5 km,
   the same number (here it's 3).   so 3 cm represents 5 × 3 = **15 km**

b) **In real life, two villages are 20 km apart.**
   How far apart are they on the map?

   Divide the real-life distance by the   5 km is represented by 1 cm,
   number of km represented by 1 cm   so 20 km is represented by
   to find the distance on the map.   20 ÷ 5 = **4 cm**

Exercise 1

1   A map scale is given as 1 cm : 2 km.

   a) Convert these lengths on the map to actual distances:

   i) 4 cm   **ii)** 5 cm

   iii) 8 cm   **iv)** 10 cm

   v) 12.5 cm   **vi)** 16.5 cm

   b) Convert these actual distances to lengths on the map:

   i) 6 km   **ii)** 14 km

   iii) 24 km   **iv)** 40 km

   v) 100 km   **vi)** 35 km

2   The distance from Manchester to Liverpool is 50 km. The scale on a map is 1 cm : 10 km.
    How far apart are they on the map?

3 A road map uses a scale of 1 cm : 20 km.
Find the actual distances represented by these lengths on the map:

a) 5 cm

b) 7 cm

c) 11 cm

d) 6.5 cm

e) 12.5 cm

f) 14.75 cm

4 An atlas uses a scale of 1 cm : 100 km.
Find the lengths on the map used to represent these actual distances:

a) 300 km

b) 800 km

c) 1000 km

d) 450 km

e) 950 km

f) 280 km

5 The distance from London to Glasgow is shown on a map as 11 cm.
The scale on the map is 1 cm : 50 km.
What is the actual distance from London to Glasgow?

6 A plan of an office building is drawn using a scale of 1 cm : 5 m.
Find the actual lengths if they are given on the plan as:

a) 2 cm

b) 5 cm

c) 8 cm

d) 3.5 cm

e) 6.5 cm

f) 4.2 cm

7 An architect is drawing the plans for a building using a scale of 1 cm : 4 m.
Find the lengths he should draw on the plan to represent these actual measurements:

a) 8 m

b) 16 m

c) 20 m

d) 10 m

e) 18 m

f) 25 m

8 The distance from New York to Las Vegas is 3600 km.
Find the length used to represent this distance on a map with a scale of 1 cm : 250 km.

9 A plan of a housing estate has a scale of 1 cm : 0.5 km.

   a) A street on the estate is 1.5 km long. How long will this street be on the plan?

   b) A different street is 2 cm long on the plan. How long is the street in real life?

   c) The park in the housing estate measures 0.25 km by 0.5 km.
   What are the dimensions of the park on the plan?

10 Ryan makes a scale model of a pirate ship using a scale of 2 cm : 5 m.
Use the actual measurements given to find the measurements on his model.

   a) Height of mast = 25 m

   b) Length of ship = 50 m

   c) Width of ship = 12.5 m

   d) Length of plank = 7.5 m

Scales without Units

A scale without units (e.g 1 : 100) means you can use any units — but you must
put the same units on both sides. For example, 1 cm : 100 cm or 1 mm : 100 mm.

> **Example 2** **The scale on a map is 1 : 100 000.**
> **What is the actual distance (in km) between**
> **two points which are 5 cm apart on the map.**
>
> 1. Write the scale down using cm
>   (to match the units given in the question).   1 cm : 100 000 cm
>
> 2. Multiply both sides of the scale   1 cm represents 100 000 cm
>   by the same number (here it's 5).   so 5 cm represents 500 000 cm
>
> 3. Give your answer using the correct units   500 000 cm = (500 000 ÷ 100) m
>   (you'll probably find it easier to convert   = 5000 m
>   500 000 cm to m first, then convert the   = (5000 ÷ 1000) km
>   distance in m into km).   = **5 km**

Exercise 2

1 A map scale is given as 1 : 100. In real life, a fountain and a tree are 600 cm apart.
How far apart are they on the map? Give your answer in cm.

2 A map scale is given as 1:1000. Two houses on the map are 5 cm apart. How far apart are they in real life? Give your answer in cm.

3 The scale on a plan is given as 1:500.

a) Convert these lengths on the plan to actual distances. Give your answers in metres.

i) 4 cm

ii) 10 cm

iii) 12 cm

iv) 15 cm

v) 6.5 cm

vi) 14.5 cm

b) Convert these actual distances to lengths on the plan. Give your answers in cm.

i) 5 m

ii) 10 m

iii) 40 m

iv) 12.5 m

v) 7.5 m

vi) 8.5 m

4 A map scale is given as 1:250. Convert these lengths on the map to actual distances. Give your answers in metres.

a) 4 cm

b) 7 cm

c) 12 cm

d) 10.5 cm

e) 18.5 cm

f) 6.6 cm

5 A map scale is given as 1:1000. Convert these actual distances to lengths on the map. Give your answers in cm.

a) 2000 cm

b) 4500 cm

c) 11 000 cm

d) 10 m

e) 15 m

f) 60 m

6 The scale on a map is 1:100 000. The distance between two towns is shown as 8 cm on the map.

a) Find the real life distance between the two towns. Leave your answer in cm.

b) Use your answer from part **a)** to find the distance between the towns in m.

c) Use your answer from part **b)** to find the distance between the towns in km.

Investigate — Scales

A piece of A4 paper is 29.7 cm long and 21 cm wide.

a) What scale would you need to use to draw a plan
of your classroom on a piece of A4 paper?
Start by estimating the length and width
of the room in m, then change this to cm.
Once you've decided on a scale, measure
the room accurately and draw it using your scale.

b) Now measure the desks and any other furniture
in your classroom, and draw them on the plan.

c) Estimate the scale you'd need to use to draw a plan of your
school on a piece of A4 paper. What scale could you use to
draw a plan of your town on a piece of A4 paper?

Scale Drawings

Scale diagrams and plans also use <u>scales</u> to show actual distances on a drawing.

Example 3 **The diagram shows a rough sketch
of a park. Use the scale 1 cm : 5 m
to draw an accurate plan of the park.**

1. Use the scale to work out the lengths for the plan.
   1 cm = 5 m, so divide the lengths in m by 5 to find
   the lengths in cm on the plan.

   5 m: 5 ÷ 5 = 1 cm
   2.5 m: 2.5 ÷ 5 = 0.5 cm
   20 m: 20 ÷ 5 = 4 cm
   10 m: 10 ÷ 5 = 2 cm

2. Use these lengths to draw an accurate plan.

Exercise 3

1   These scale drawings have been drawn using the scale 1 cm : 1 m.
    Measure the scale drawings and use the scale to find the actual lengths
    of sides a, b and c in each shape.

a)

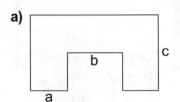

b)

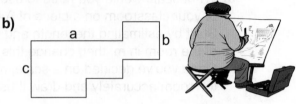

2   A sketch of part of a zoo has been drawn.

   a) Use the scale 1 cm : 5 m to draw an
      accurate plan of the zoo.

   b) Use your plan to find the real-life distance between
      the two points labelled A and B on the sketch.
      Give your answer to the nearest metre.

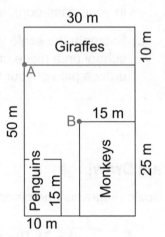

3   Tyler has drawn a scale drawing of his garden
    using the scale 1 cm : 2 m.

   a) Find the actual dimensions of the patio.

   b) Find the actual dimensions of the vegetable patch.

   c) Copy the scale drawing and draw on a flower bed
      with actual dimensions 2 m by 2 m.

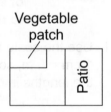

4   Isabel has made a sketch of her shed.
    Draw an accurate plan of the shed, using a scale of 1 : 50.

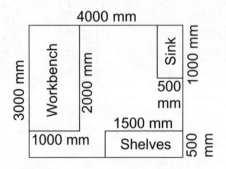

Section 8 — Algebraic Express

8.1 Expressions

An algebraic <u>expression</u> uses letters (called <u>variables</u>) to represent
Expressions do not contain an equals sign (=).

An expression consists of a number of <u>terms</u> separated by + or – sig
Terms can be letters, numbers, or a mixture of both.

Each term has a + or a – sign attached to the front of it.
Terms at the start of an expression which don't have a sign in front of them are <u>positive</u>.

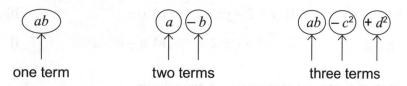

one term   two terms   three terms

In expressions, there is a standard algebraic notation (a kind of 'shorthand')
which is used to write terms more easily:

$$ab = a \times b$$
$$3y = 3 \times y \ (\text{or } y + y + y)$$
$$a^2 = a \times a$$
$$3a^2 = 3a \times a \ (\text{or } 3 \times a \times a \text{ or } 3 \times a^2)$$

$$a^3 = a \times a \times a$$
$$a^2b = a \times a \times b$$
$$\frac{a}{b} = a \div b$$

A <u>coefficient</u> is a value placed before a variable in an algebraic expression,
e.g. the '5' in $5y$. Non-integer coefficients are normally written as fractions, not decimals.

Example 1 **Write each of these as a single term:**

a) **$4p \times 5p$**

Multiply numbers and letters separately. $4 \times 5 \times p \times p$

$$20p^2$$

b) **$2w \times 3y$**

Multiply numbers and letters
separately.

$2 \times 3 \times w \times y$

$6wy$

...w many terms are in each of these expressions?

a) $6y + z - c$ **b)** $a + b$ **c)** $3r - 7 + u$ **d)** $11b + x - 3$

e) ab **f)** $ab + 7$ **g)** $6 + c + xy$ **h)** $abc + 9$

i) $2v + x^2$ **j)** $ab^2 - b$ **k)** $3 + c^3$ **l)** $12 - abc + d^3$

2 List the terms that are in each of these expressions. Remember to include signs.

a) $m + 9 + n$ **b)** $a - bc + d^2$ **c)** $11r - 2 + t$ **d)** $-p - q + 7$

e) $ab + cd$ **f)** $y + 7 - yz$ **g)** xyz **h)** $q - rs + 4 + t$

i) $f^2 + g^2h$ **j)** $-v^2 - v + 2$ **k)** $8 - c^3 - c^2$ **l)** $1 - xyz + z^3 - y$

3 Write each of these expressions as a single term.

a) $y \times y \times y$ **b)** $n \times n \times n$ **c)** $q \times q \times q \times q$

d) $a \times a$ **e)** $a \times b \times b$ **f)** $2m \times 3m$

g) $8r \times 2r$ **h)** $5x \times 3x$ **i)** $9y \times 2y$

j) $6d \times 4d$ **k)** $3s \times 7t$ **l)** $11i \times 12k$

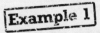

8.2 Simplifying Expressions

Expressions can sometimes be <u>simplified</u> by collecting <u>like terms</u>.
'Like terms' contain exactly the same letters, but may contain different numbers.

Example 1 **By collecting like terms, simplify this expression:**
$7w + 5w - 2w$

1. This expression contains three terms.
   The only letter in each term is w,
   so they are three like terms.

2. So start with $7w$ and add $5w$
   — this gives $12w$.

   $7w + 5w - 2w = 12w - 2w$

   Then subtract $2w$ to give the final answer. $= 10w$

Exercise 1

1   Simplify these expressions.

a) $2y + 7y$

b) $9b - 3b$

c) $7d - 4d$

d) $t + 12t$

e) $6x - x$

f) $5y + 4y$

g) $p + 9p$

h) $8s - 7s$

i) $6w - w$

j) $14n + n$

2   Simplify these expressions.

a) $6d + 5d - 2d$

b) $9x + 6x - 8x$

c) $3w + 8w + 4w$

d) $10y - 8y - y$

e) $8t + 4t - 6t$

f) $8n - 5n + 2n$

g) $12s + 10s - 7s$

h) $4z + z - 2z$

i) $6g - 2g + g$

j) $9a + a - 6a - 2a$

k) $12x + x - 4x - 3x$

l) $8w + w - 4w - 3w$

m) $8r + r - 6r - 2r$

n) $19h + h - 5h - 12h$

o) $16n + n - 4n - 2n$

Example 2   **Simplify the expression $6a + 2b - 4a - 8b$.**

1. '$6a$' and '$-4a$' are like terms. '$2b$' and '$-8b$' are like terms.

2. Rewrite the expression with the
   like terms collected together.

   $6a - 4a + 2b - 8b$

3. Combine the like terms.

   $6a - 4a = 2a$
   $2b - 8b = -6b$

4. Write out the simplified expression.

   $2a - 6b$

---

3   Simplify these expressions.

a) $2x + x + 3y + y$

b) $4a - a + 6b + 2b$

c) $9m - 3m + n + 4n$

d) $p + 5q + 2p - 4q$

e) $6f - 5g - 2g + 3f$

f) $3a + 3c - a + 3c$

g) $4x - 3x - 5y - y$

h) $2p + q + 4p - 6q$

i) $6f + 7g - 2f - 3g$

j) $10s - 4t - 2s + 6t$

k) $7x + 2y - y - x$

l) $8m + 4n - n + 7m$

m) $5d + 3e - 8e - d$

n) $11p - 6q - 3p - 8q$

o) $-7i + 3j - 5i - 6j$

4 Simplify these expressions. Terms with no letters can be added together, or subtracted.

a) $f + 4 + 11f + 9$

b) $5x + 8 + 12x + 4$

c) $9y - 6y - 11 + 6$

d) $s + 2s + 6 - 12$

e) $9f + 12 - 2 - 2f$

f) $6a - a + 14 - 3$

g) $12 + 7x - 2x - 5$

h) $2q + 7q + 11 - 12$

i) $3 - 2g + 7g - 10$

j) $10 - 6y + 7y - 3$

k) $11s + 12 + 10 - 7s$

l) $-4 + 6h - 4h - 11$

5 Add together the following pairs of expressions and simplify your answer.

a) $4y + 2x$ and $7y - 5x$

b) $8c + 6d$ and $6c + d$

c) $11r - 2s$ and $5r + 8s$

d) $12g + 4j$ and $-15g - 7j$

e) $11w - 5u$ and $5w - 11u$

f) $-9y + 11z$ and $12y - 15z$

g) $-7v - 3w$ and $8v - 10w$

h) $12g + 5h$ and $g - 11h$

8.3 Expressions with Brackets

Expanding Brackets

You can 'expand' (or remove) brackets by multiplying everything inside the brackets by the letter or number in front.

$$a(b + c) = ab + ac$$
$$a(b - c) = ab - ac$$

Remember — you can write $a \times b$ as ab.

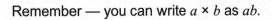

Example 1 **Expand the brackets in these expressions:**

a) **$4(z + 3)$**

Multiply both z and 3 by 4.

$(4 \times z) + (4 \times 3)$

$4z + 12$

b) **$5(y - 1)$**

Multiply both y and 1 by 5.

$(5 \times y) - (5 \times 1)$

$5y - 5$

Expand the brackets in these expressions:

a) $a(b + 2)$

Multiply both b and 2 by a.

$(a \times b) + (a \times 2)$

$ab + 2a$

b) $g(g - 6)$

Multiply both g and 6 by g.

$(g \times g) - (g \times 6)$

$g^2 - 6g$

Exercise 1

1 Expand the brackets in the following expressions.

a) $3(c + 2)$ **b)** $4(d + 6)$ **c)** $2(r + 7)$

d) $5(4 + x)$ **e)** $9(g - 1)$ **f)** $11(f - 8)$

g) $12(3 + m)$ **h)** $7(1 - e)$ **i)** $6(8 + c)$

2 Expand the brackets in the following expressions.

a) $d(e + 2)$ **b)** $x(y - 7)$ **c)** $w(h - 4)$

d) $s(6 + t)$ **e)** $m(3 + p)$ **f)** $x(8 - y)$

g) $g(g + 10)$ **h)** $p(p + 3)$ **i)** $s(s - 9)$

j) $m(11 + m)$ **k)** $y(6 + y)$ **l)** $z(12 + z)$

Expand the brackets in the following expressions:

a) $6(2h - 3)$

1. Multiply both $2h$ and 3 by 6.

$(6 \times 2h) - (6 \times 3)$

2. Multiply the numbers in the first term together.

$(6 \times 2 \times h) - (6 \times 3)$

$12h - 18$

b) $4n(q + 2n)$

1. Multiply both q and $2n$ by $4n$.

$(4n \times q) + (4n \times 2n)$

2. Multiply numbers and letters separately in each term.

$(4 \times n \times q) + (6 \times 2 \times n \times n)$

$4nq + 12n^2$

3 Expand the brackets in the following expressions.

    a) $4(3n + 8)$ **b)** $2(6p - 3)$ **c)** $6(9q + 1)$

    d) $9(7x + 5)$ **e)** $3(4y - 2)$ **f)** $4(6 + 4w)$

    g) $12(11 + 2c)$ **h)** $7(9 - 6d)$ **i)** $4(5 - 5g)$

4 Expand the brackets in the following expressions.

    a) $2a(5a - 9)$ **b)** $4d(3d + 7)$ **c)** $5g(12g - 5)$

    d) $6n(n + 4)$ **e)** $3x(11 + 2x)$ **f)** $2y(6 - 12y)$

    g) $12t(4t - 11)$ **h)** $10w(2w + 9)$ **i)** $7p(9 + 6p)$

5 Expand the brackets in the following expressions.

    a) $4(2v - x)$ **b)** $2(b - 6c)$ **c)** $8(g + 5h)$

    d) $11(4f + n)$ **e)** $4p(3p + 4s)$ **f)** $3t(2t + 8n)$

    g) $2u(8k - 3u)$ **h)** $5h(r + 7h)$ **i)** $6v(9v + 5m)$

Investigate — Expanding Brackets

You can multiply pairs of brackets together using the grid method.
Follow steps **a)-c)** to work out $(x + 2)$ by $(x + 3)$

a) Draw out a 3 × 3 grid. Put x and 2 on top.
Then put x and 3 down the side.

×	x	2
x		
3		

b) Fill in the missing numbers by multiplying each row by each column.

c) Add together the terms in the 4 boxes.
Can you simplify this expression?

d) Can you use this method to multiply other pairs of expressions?
Try $(a + 6) \times (a + 5)$ and $(y + 4) \times (y + 3)$.

e) Can you spot any patterns in your answers?

Factorising

Factorising is the opposite of expanding brackets. It's putting brackets into an expression.

You look for the highest common factor (HCF) of all the terms in an expression, and 'take it outside' a pair of brackets.

Example 4 Factorise $12p + 8$

1. 4 is the highest common factor of $12p$ and 8.
   So write a pair of brackets with a 4 outside.

   $12p + 8 = 4(\ +\ )$

2. Divide each term in the expression by the common factor and write the results in the brackets.

   $12p \div 4 = 3p$

   $8 \div 4 = 2$

   $4(3p + 2)$

Exercise 2

1 a) Find the highest common factor of $9a$ and 27.

   b) Divide both $9a$ and 27 by your answer to **a)**.

   c) Using your answers to **a)** and **b)**, factorise the expression $9a + 27$.

2 a) Find the highest common factor of $12b$ and 16.

   b) Divide both $12b$ and 16 by your answer to **a)**.

   c) Using your answers to **a)** and **b)**, factorise the expression $12b - 16$.

3 a) Find the highest common factor of 15 and $24x$.

   b) Factorise the expression $15 - 24x$.

4 Factorise these expressions.

   a) $9 + 18a$ **b)** $12 + 4b$ **c)** $5 - 25c$ **d)** $8x + 20$

   e) $6d - 33$ **f)** $12x + 60$ **g)** $14y + 49$ **h)** $35 + 15v$

   i) $8c - 52$ **j)** $16p - 12$ **k)** $110 - 33x$ **l)** $18x + 66$

Section 9 — Equations

9.1 Solving Equations

One-Step Equations

An <u>equation</u> has an <u>expression</u> on each side of an equals sign. <u>Solving</u> an equation means finding the value of an unknown letter that makes both sides <u>equal</u>.

For example, the <u>solution</u> of $2a + 4 = 10$ is $a = 3$ (because if $a = 3$, both sides equal 10).

Example 1   **Solve the equation $y + 9 = 13$.**

1. You need to get y on its own on one side of the equation so subtract 9 from the left-hand side. $y + 9 = 13$

2. Always do the same to both sides of an equation. $\quad y + 9 - 9 = 13 - 9$
   So subtract 9 from the right-hand side too.

3. Now find the solution to the equation. $y = 13 - 9$

     $y = 4$

Example 2   **Solve the equation $28 - x = 6$.**

1. Add x to both sides of the equation — this gets $28 - x = 6$
   rid of the minus sign in front of x. $28 - x + x = 6 + x$

2. Now you can solve the equation as before. $28 = x + 6$
   Subtract 6 from both sides of the equation... $28 - 6 = x + 6 - 6$

3. ... and find the solution. Always write your $28 - 6 = x$
   answer with the letter on the left-hand side. $x = 22$

Exercise 1

1   Solve these equations to find a value for x.

    a) $x + 4 = 9$ **b)** $x + 14 = 36$ **c)** $x - 5 = 54$ **d)** $x - 13 = 20$

    e) $x - 37 = 50$ **f)** $x - 12 = 17$ **g)** $13 + x = 18$ **h)** $9 + x = 22$

    i) $50 = x + 2$ **j)** $45 = x + 6$ **k)** $17 = x - 3$ **l)** $20 = x - 6$

    m) $42 = 11 + x$ **n)** $12 = 7 + x$ **o)** $x - 56 = 0$ **p)** $41 = x + 27$

2 Solve these equations.

a) $6 - x = 3$ b) $18 - x = 5$ c) $22 - x = 17$ d) $12 - x = 0$

e) $20 - x = 13$ f) $35 - x = 32$ g) $56 - x = 46$ h) $63 - x = 59$

i) $77 - x = 62$ j) $24 - x = 3$ k) $36 - x = 12$ l) $17 - x = 11$

m) $60 = 70 - x$ n) $42 = 50 - x$ o) $12 = 18 - x$ p) $39 = 43 - x$

q) $18 = 20 - x$ r) $30 = 44 - x$ s) $17 = 25 - x$ t) $6 = 35 - x$

3 Solve the following equations.

a) $p + 5 = 10$ b) $b + 12 = 19$ c) $y - 3 = 0$ d) $x - 0 = 17$

e) $t + 15 = 30$ f) $17 - s = 2$ g) $36 = 58 - n$ h) $z + 8 = 27$

i) $25 = n + 12$ j) $35 - y = 24$ k) $x + 16 = 26$ l) $50 = 63 - t$

m) $0 = 16 - m$ n) $p - 15 = 12$ o) $r + 5 = 17$ p) $y - 3 = 18$

q) $82 = 83 - t$ r) $51 - y = 14$ s) $x - 12 = 11$ t) $s + 6 = 94$

Example 3	Solve the equation $3m = 36$.

1. Get m on its own by dividing both sides of the equation by 3. $3m = 36$
   $3m \div 3 = 36 \div 3$

2. Remember: $3m \div 3 = m$ $m = 12$

Exercise 2

1 Solve the following equations to find a value for x.

a) $5x = 15$ b) $2x = 24$ c) $3x = 18$ d) $6x = 42$

e) $8x = 48$ f) $11x = 121$ g) $7x = 56$ h) $4x = 36$

i) $9x = 108$ j) $2x = 56$ k) $4x = 52$ l) $10x = 210$

2 Solve the following equations to find a value for y.

a) $18 = 6y$ **b)** $25 = 5y$ **c)** $54 = 9y$

d) $40 = 8y$ **e)** $56 = 7y$ **f)** $14 = 2y$

g) $27 = 3y$ **h)** $100 = 10y$ **i)** $32 = 4y$

j) $132 = 11y$ **k)** $48 = 12y$ **l)** $26 = 2y$

m) $180 = 10y$ **n)** $42 = 3y$ **o)** $90 = 5y$

3 Use a calculator to solve the equations below. Write your answers as decimals.

a) $8m = 36$ **b)** $40n = 50$ **c)** $36a = 90$

d) $8x = 12$ **e)** $30y = 75$ **f)** $5x = 16$

g) $15y = 39$ **h)** $20t = 75$ **i)** $16z = 68$

j) $16p = 36$ **k)** $34r = 119$ **l)** $8p = 18$

4 Use a calculator to solve the equations below. Write your answers as decimals.

a) $57 = 38p$ **b)** $20 = 16b$

c) $55 = 25z$ **d)** $54 = 12s$

e) $28 = 8r$ **f)** $42 = 24n$

g) $77 = 28a$ **h)** $162 = 36y$

i) $42 = 15x$ **j)** $39 = 15y$

k) $85 = 20t$ **l)** $60 = 16x$

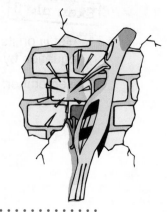

> ### Investigate — Solving Equations
>
> **a)** Work out the answer to this problem in your head:
> *"I think of a number, multiply it by 2 and subtract 5.
> I end up with 43. What was the number I thought of?"*
>
> **b)** Now try and write down the steps you used to solve it.
>
> **c)** Make up a few of these problems of your own, then write
> some instructions for how to solve them. Try writing them
> out as algebraic equations if you can.

Two-Step Equations

Some equations need to be solved in two stages.
You need to do the stages in the right order.

> ### Example 4 — Solve the equation $3n + 4 = 19$.
>
> $3n + 4$ means "take your value of n and then:
>   i) multiply it by 3,
>   ii) add 4".
>
> To get n on its own, "undo" these steps, but in the opposite order.
>
> First, subtract 4 from both sides.
>
> $$3n + 4 - 4 = 19 - 4$$
> $$3n = 15$$
>
> Then divide both sides by 3.
>
> $$3n \div 3 = 15 \div 3$$
> $$n = 5$$
>
> Check your answer by putting the value of n back into the equation:
>
> $$(3 \times 5) + 4 = 15 + 4 = 19$$

Exercise 3

1 Solve these equations to find a value for x.

a) $4x + 8 = 40$

b) $5x + 6 = 41$

c) $2x + 13 = 25$

d) $3x + 6 = 24$

e) $2x + 12 = 72$

f) $4x + 9 = 33$

g) $10x + 3 = 43$

h) $12x + 17 = 65$

i) $11x + 3 = 135$

2 Solve the following equations.

a) $3p - 6 = 24$

b) $5s - 2 = 28$

c) $2t - 9 = 7$

d) $4r - 12 = 20$

e) $11m - 17 = 16$

f) $9n - 10 = 44$

g) $12y - 8 = 88$

h) $8x - 4 = 52$

i) $7z - 36 = 48$

3 Solve the following equations.

a) $8 + 2x = 30$

b) $1 + 5x = 16$

c) $15 + 3x = 45$

d) $7 + 11x = 84$

e) $42 - 6x = 6$

f) $45 - 7x = 3$

g) $98 - 10x = 38$

h) $32 - 5x = 17$

i) $47 = 12 + 7x$

j) $32 = 4 + 4x$

k) $72 = 36 + 9x$

l) $41 = 11 + 10x$

Section 10 — Formulas

10.1 Writing Formulas

A <u>formula</u> is like a set of instructions for working something out.

For example, $s = r + 1$ is a formula for s. It tells you how to find s if you know the value of r.

The '$r + 1$' part is called an <u>expression</u>.

Example 1   Write a formula for a in terms of b if:

a) **a is two less than b**

You need to subtract 2 from b to get a. $a = b - 2$

b) **a is double b**

You need to multiply b by 2 to get a. $a = 2 \times b$, so $a = 2b$

Exercise 1

1   Write a formula for a in terms of b if:

a) a is 2 more than b b) a is 100 more than b

c) a is 4 less than b d) a is 2.5 less than b

e) a is 7 times as big as b f) a is 10 times as big as b

g) a is half of b h) a is the same as b

i) a is $\dfrac{1}{3}$ of b j) a is double b

2   Write out these formulas in words.
The first one has been done for you.

a) $a = b - 5$ becomes   "***a* is 5 less than *b***"

b) $x = y - 6$ c) $T = 14 + Q$

d) $g = h + 9$ e) $l = 3m$

f) $c = 100e$ g) $q = r$

h) $j = \dfrac{1}{4}k$ i) $p = \dfrac{2}{3}h$

j) $z = 4y$ k) $t = 14v$

Example 2

Example 2 **I have m coins and my friend has n coins.**
I have three times as many coins as him.
Write a formula for the number of coins I have.

1. "My friend has n coins." n

2. "I have three times as many..." — so you need
   to multiply the amount my friend has by 3. $3 \times n = 3n$

3. "I have m coins..." — so you
   need to put m equal to $3n$. $m = 3n$

3 Kym has a tin containing n biscuits. She eats 2 of the biscuits.
Write a formula for m, the number of biscuits she has left.

4 Krissie has r crayons. A friend gives her 5 more crayons.
Write a formula for s, the number of crayons Krissie now has.

5 A lemur has t figs. The lemur loses 10 figs.
Write a formula for u, the number of figs the lemur has left.

6 Pat buys x balloons for his party. He pops 1 balloon before the party starts.
Write a formula for y, the number of balloons he has left for the party.

7 Carl drives 4.5 miles to the bowling alley. He then drives n miles further.
Write a formula for p, the number of miles Carl drives in total.

8 Thelma has a DVDs. Gregory has 5 times as many DVDs as Thelma.
Write a formula for b, the number of DVDs Gregory has.

9 Sean has s geese. Zilda has 8 times as many geese as Sean.
Write a formula for c, the number of geese Zilda has.

10 For every hour Rachel works in a day, Peter works two hours.
Today Rachel worked q hours.
Write a formula for w, the number of hours Peter worked today.

11 Joe spends m minutes on his piano practice.
Tony spends half as long as Joe on his piano practice.
Write a formula for h, the number of minutes Tony spends on his piano practice.

12 Callum runs x metres each day.
Johnny runs a third of the distance that Callum runs each day.
Write a formula for y, the distance Johnny runs each day.

13 Keith has d ducks — four times as many as me.
Write a formula for c, the number of ducks I have.

14 Trish has c flowers, which is 7 times as many as Terry.
Write a formula for f, the number of flowers Terry has.

15 Len has 5 ties, which is s more than Rod.
Write a formula for r, the number of ties Rod has.

16 Jessica is j years old. She is 3 years younger than Kai, who is k years old.

  a) Write a formula for Jessica's age in terms of Kai's age.

  b) Write a formula for Kai's age in terms of Jessica's age.

Investigate — Writing Formulas

  a) This square has a side of length a.
  What are the lengths of the other sides?

  b) What is the perimeter? Can you write this as a single term?
  Can you write a formula for the perimeter, P, of the square?

  c) What's the perimeter, P, of a rectangle
  with length a and width b?

  d) Can you make rules for any other shapes?

10.2 Substituting into a Formula

Substituting into Expressions and Formulas

Substituting numbers into an <u>expression</u> or a <u>formula</u> means replacing letters with numbers.

> **Example 1** $S = 3r$. **Find the value of S when $r = 5$.**
>
> 1. Write down the formula.
>
> $S = 3r$
>
> 2. $3r$ means $3 \times r$.
>   Replace r with 5 and do the calculation.
>
> $S = 3 \times 5 = \mathbf{15}$

Exercise 1

1 If x is 2, what is:

    a) $x + 3$?   **b)** $x - 1$?

2 If d is 6, what is:

    a) $2d$?   **b)** $d \div 3$?

3 Find the value of s in each of the following when $t = 2$.

    a) $s = 4 + t$ **b)** $s = 2 + t$ **c)** $s = t - 1$ **d)** $s = 5 - t$

4 If $q = 8$ and $r = 6$, find the value of s in each of the following.

    a) $s = q + 3$ **b)** $s = r - 2$ **c)** $s = q + r$ **d)** $s = q - r$

5 $B = 5c$. Find the value of B when:

    a) $c = 3$ **b)** $c = 7$ **c)** $c = 20$ **d)** $c = 100$

6 Find the value of y in each of the following when $x = 4$.

    a) $y = \dfrac{8}{x}$ **b)** $y = \dfrac{16}{x}$ **c)** $y = \dfrac{20}{x}$ **d)** $y = \dfrac{40}{x}$

> **Example 2** The cost of hiring a bike is worked out using the
> formula $C = 5h + 10$, where C is the cost in pounds
> and h is the number of hours the bike is hired for.
>
> Use the formula to work out the cost of hiring a bike for 4 hours.
>
> 1. Write down the formula.
> 2. Replace h with the number of hours (4), and do the calculation.
>
> $C = 5h + 10$
> $= (5 \times 4) + 10$
> $= 20 + 10 = 30$
>
> So it costs **£30** to hire
> a bike for 4 hours

Exercise 2

1 Find the value of G in each of the following if $h = 2$.

    a) $G = 2h + 1$ **b)** $G = 40 - 4h$ **c)** $G = 7 - 3h$ **d)** $G = 9 + 3h$

2 If $x = 4$ and $y = 2$, find the value of z in each of the following.

    a) $z = x - y$ **b)** $z = x + y$ **c)** $z = x + \dfrac{y}{2}$ **d)** $z = 3x + 3y$

3 A teacher hires a coach for a school trip. The cost is worked out using the formula
$C = \dfrac{m}{3} + 15$, where C is the cost in pounds and m is the number of miles the coach travels.

Work out how much it would cost to hire the coach for a distance of:

    a) 9 miles   **b)** 15 miles   **c)** 30 miles   **d)** 300 miles

4 The price of a bag of pick 'n' mix sweets in pence, S, is worked out using the formula
$S = 2w + 15$, where w is the weight of the sweets in grams.

Work out how much bags of sweets with the following weights will cost:

    a) 100 g   **b)** 50 g   **c)** 120 g   **d)** 60 g

5 The cost of hiring a boat is worked out using $C = 5h + 4$,
where C is the cost in pounds and h is the number of hours the boat is hired for.
Find the cost of hiring a boat for two hours.

Using Formulas in Maths and Science

Formulas are used a lot in maths and science. Here are some examples:

$$\text{area of rectangle} = \text{length} \times \text{width}$$
$$A = l \times w$$

$$\text{speed} = \frac{\text{distance}}{\text{time}}$$

$$\text{volume of cuboid} = \text{length} \times \text{width} \times \text{height}$$
$$V = l \times w \times h$$

Exercise 3

1 The formula for finding the perimeter of a square, P, can be written as $P = 4l$, where l is the length of one side. Work out the perimeter of a square with a side length of 7 cm.

2 The formula for the area of a rectangle, A, is $A = lw$.
Work out the area of a rectangle with a length, l, of 9 m and a width, w, of 11 m.

3 The distance Kyle rides on his motorbike can be worked out using this formula:

$$\text{distance} = \text{speed} \times \text{time}$$

Work out the distance Kyle rides in miles if he rides at 45 mph for 2 hours.

4 Use the formula to work out the area of this triangle.

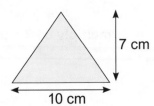

7 cm

10 cm

$$\text{area of triangle} = \frac{1}{2} \times \text{base} \times \text{height}$$

5 Force, F, can be calculated using the formula $F = ma$. Work out the value of F when:

a) $m = 10$, $a = 3$ **b)** $m = 4$, $a = 14$ **c)** $m = 12$, $a = 9$

d) $m = 0.5$, $a = 18$ **e)** $m = 5$, $a = 2.5$ **f)** $m = 1.5$, $a = 3.5$

Section 11 — Sequences

11.1 Term-to-Term Rules

Finding the Rule

A <u>sequence</u> is an ordered list of <u>terms</u>.

The rule for extending (continuing) the sequence tells you how to find the next term.

Example 1 **Find the rule for extending the sequence:**

6, 10, 14, 18, 22

1. Write the difference between neighbouring terms in the gaps.

   6   10   14   18   22
       +4 +4 +4 +4

2. Identify the rule.   **"add 4 each time"**

Example 2 **Find the rule for extending the sequence:**

2, 6, 18, 54, 162

1. First, try writing the difference between the neighbouring terms.

   2   6   18   54   162
     +4 +12 +36 +108

2. If this doesn't give an obvious 'addition' rule, see if each term is being multiplied by some number.

   2   6   18   54   162
     ×3 ×3 ×3 ×3

3. This works, so the rule is: **"multiply by 3 each time"**

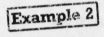

Exercise 1

1 a) Write out the first five odd numbers, starting at 1.

   b) What is the rule for extending the sequence of odd numbers?

2 What is the rule for extending the sequence of even numbers?

3 Find the rule for extending each of the following sequences:

    a) 1, 5, 9, 13, 17...

    b) 4, 7, 10, 13, 16...

    c) 6, 8, 10, 12, 14...

    d) 8, 15, 22, 29, 36, 43...

    e) 21, 31, 41, 51, 61...

    f) 11, 19, 27, 35, 43...

    g) 5, 17, 29, 41, 53...

    h) 2, 11, 20, 29, 38...

4 Find the rule for extending each of the following sequences:

    a) 20, 17, 14, 11, 8...

    b) 13, 11, 9, 7, 5...

    c) 40, 36, 32, 28, 24...

    d) 50, 45, 40, 35, 30...

    e) 38, 32, 26, 20, 14...

    f) 108, 103, 98, 93, 88...

    g) 150, 139, 128, 117, 106...

    h) 284, 276, 268, 260, 252...

5 Find the rule for extending each of the following sequences:

    a) 24, 18, 12, 6, 0...

    b) 5, 11, 17, 23, 29...

    c) 32, 43, 54, 65, 76...

    d) 34, 49, 64, 79, 94...

    e) 18, 32, 46, 60, 74...

    f) 102, 84, 66, 48, 30...

    g) 12, 7, 2, –3, –8...

    h) 412, 388, 364, 340, 316...

6 Find the rule for extending each of the following sequences:

    a) 1, 4, 16, 64, 256...

    b) 1, 5, 25, 125, 625...

    c) 3, 9, 27, 81, 243...

    d) 4, 8, 16, 32, 64...

    e) 5, 20, 80, 320, 1280...

    f) 6, 30, 150, 750, 3750...

    g) 11, 33, 99, 297, 891...

    h) 3, 21, 147, 1029, 7203...

7 Find the rule for extending each of the following sequences:

    a) 80, 40, 20, 10, 5...

    b) 162, 54, 18, 6, 2...

    c) 24, 12, 6, 3, 1.5...

    d) 128, 32, 8, 2, 0.5...

    e) 567, 189, 63, 21, 7...

    f) 576, 144, 36, 9, 2.25...

    g) 1536, 384, 96, 24, 6...

    h) 2592, 432, 72, 12, 2...

8 Find the rule for extending each of the following sequences:

a) 24, 31, 38, 45, 52...

b) 54, 41, 28, 15, 2...

c) 20 000, 2000, 200, 20, 2...

d) 3, 35, 67, 99, 131...

e) 7, 63, 567, 5103, 45 927...

f) 36, 18, 0, –18, –36...

g) 3750, 750, 150, 30, 6...

h) –13, –8, –3, 2, 7...

i) 21, 105, 525, 2625, 13 125...

j) 13, 25, 37, 49, 61...

k) 6400, 1600, 400, 100, 25...

l) –20, –15, –10, –5, 0...

m) 20, 10, 5, 2.5, 1.25...

n) 0.05, 0.5, 5, 50, 500...

Finding Terms

To write down a <u>sequence</u> you need to know two things:

1. The **first** term of the sequence.

2. The rule for **extending** the sequence.

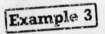 **Example 3** The first term of a sequence is 4 and the rule is "add 6 each time". Write down the first five terms.

1. Add six to the first term to find the second term. $4 + 6 = 10$

2. Now add six to the second term to find the third term. Carry on until you have five terms.
$$10 + 6 = 16$$
$$16 + 6 = 22$$
$$22 + 6 = 28$$

3. Write out the first five terms of the sequence.   **4, 10, 16, 22, 28**

Exercise 2

1 Write down the first **five** terms of each of these sequences:

a) The first term is 7 and the rule is "add 2 each time".

b) The first term is 18 and the rule is "subtract 4 each time".

c) The first term is 3 and the rule is "multiply by 4 each time".

d) The first term is 4375 and the rule is "divide by 5 each time".

2   Write down the first **six** terms of each of these sequences:

    a) Start at 17 and add 24 each time.

    b) Start at 88 and take away 13 each time.

    c) Start at 6 and multiply by 4 each time.

    d) Start at 4000 and divide by 10 each time.

3   The rule for extending a sequence is "add 6 each time".
    Find the first **five** terms of the sequence if the first term is:

    a) 42   **b)** 27   **c)** 0.5

4   The rule for extending a sequence is "subtract 12 each time".
    Find the first **five** terms of the sequence if the first term is:

    a) 52   **b)** 89   **c)** 61

5   The rule for extending a sequence is "multiply by 7 each time".
    Find the first **five** terms of the sequence if the first term is:

    a) 8   **b)** 14   **c)** 21

6   The rule for extending a sequence is "divide by 4 each time".
    Find the first **five** terms of the sequence if the first term is:

    a) 768   **b)** 1792   **c)** 3328

7   For each of the sequences, find:
    i) the rule for extending the sequence,
    ii) the next **two** terms in the sequence.

    a) 3, 12, 21...   **b)** 8, 14, 20...

    c) 29, 23, 17...   **d)** 37, 33, 29...

    e) 41, 54, 67...   **f)** 82, 67, 52...

    g) 12, 26, 40...   **h)** 700, 650, 600...

8 For each of the sequences, find:
i) the rule for extending the sequence,
ii) the next **two** terms in the sequence.

a) 2, 14, 98...   b) 6, 60, 600...   c) 12, 24, 48...   d) 30 000, 3000, 300...

Investigate — The Fibonacci Sequence

The Fibonacci Sequence is a particular sequence of numbers named after an Italian mathematician.
The first few terms are:

1, 1, 2, 3, 5, 8...

a) Can you find the rule for extending the sequence?

b) What are the next five terms in the sequence?

c) Draw a pattern of shapes made of dots to represent the sequence.

d) Write some different sequences based on the same rule, but with different starting numbers.

e) Make up some other sequences with different and unusual rules. Ask someone else to crack your sequences.

Shape Sequences

Example 4 The shapes made from these matchsticks form a sequence. How many matchsticks are needed to make the next shape in the sequence?

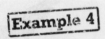

4   7   10

1. Make a sequence of numbers by writing the number of matchsticks in each shape underneath it.

2. Use these numbers to work out the rule for extending the sequence.

"add 3 each time"

3. Find the next term in the sequence.

10 + 3 = 13
So **13** matchsticks are needed.

Exercise 3

1   For each of these sequences: **i)** write down the number of dots in each shape
                                    ii) find the rule for extending the sequence
                                    iii) draw the next **two** shapes in the sequence.

   a)    b)

2   Draw the next two shapes in each of these sequences.

   a)    b)

3   How many matchsticks are needed to make the next shape in each of these sequences?

   a)    b)

   c) 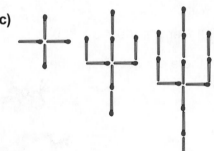   d)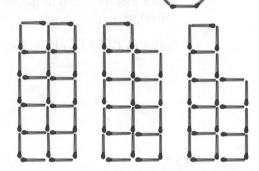

4   Work out how many squares there will be in the next two shapes
    in each of these sequences.

   a) 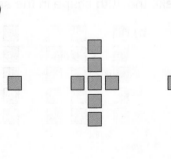   b)

11.2 Position-to-Term Rules

To work out a term at a given position in a <u>sequence</u> (say the 100th position), you can use the position-to-term rule.

Example 1 How many dots would be in the 100th shape in this sequence?

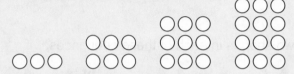

1. Draw a table with the position in the top row and the number of dots in the bottom row.

Position	1	2	3	4
Number of dots	3	6	9	12

2. Find the connection between the top row and the bottom row.

1   2   3   4
↓×3 ↓×3 ↓×3 ↓×3
3   6   9   12

3. Write this as a rule to get from the 'position' to the 'term'.

"multiply the position by 3"

4. Use this rule to find the 100th term.

100th term = 100 × 3 = 300

So there are **300** dots in the 100th shape.

Exercise 1

1   For each of these sequences,
     i) Write down the number of squares in each of the first three terms.
     ii) Find a rule to get from the position to the term.
     iii) Work out the number of squares needed to make the 10th shape in the sequence.

a)

b)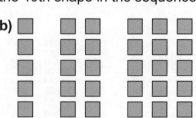

2 For each of these sequences, use a position to term rule to find the number of dots in the:

    i) 10th shape   **ii)** 100th shape

a)
    b)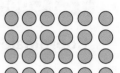

c)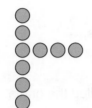
    d)

3 For each of these number sequences, find the 100th term.

    a) 2, 4, 6, 8...   **b)** 9, 18, 27, 36...

    c) 12, 24, 36, 48...   **d)** 11, 22, 33, 44...

    e) 7, 14, 21, 28...   **f)** 13, 26, 39, 52...

    g) 6, 12, 18, 24...   **h)** 15, 30, 45, 60...

    i) 100, 200, 300, 400...   **j)** −1, −2, −3, −4...

Investigate — Making Squares

Here's a sequence of dots which make a square pattern.

    a) Can you work out the rule to get from the position to the term?

    b) How many dots would be in the 10th pattern?

    c) Try drawing out the 10th pattern to check your rule.

    d) How many dots do you think there will be in the 100th pattern?

Section 12 — Graphs and Equations

12.1 Coordinates

Coordinates

Coordinates tell you the position of a point on a grid.
The grid is made by the x-axis (which goes across) and the
y-axis (which goes up and down).

Coordinates are written in pairs inside brackets,
with the x-coordinate (across) first and the
y-coordinate (up and down) second.

The place where the x- and y-axes cross is called the origin.
It has coordinates (0, 0).

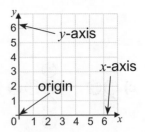

Example 1 Write down the coordinates of points *A*, *B* and *C*
shown on the graph.

1. Follow the grid line down from each
   point and read off the x-coordinate.

2. Follow the grid line across from each
   point and read off the y-coordinate.

3. Write the coordinates in brackets with
   the x-coordinate first.

The coordinates are: *A***(2, 2)**, *B***(4, 8)**, *C***(8, 4)**

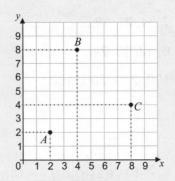

Exercise 1

1 Find the x-coordinate of points *A-C*.

a)
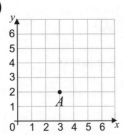

b)
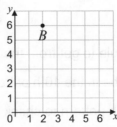

c)
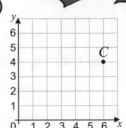

2 Find the *y*-coordinate of points *D-F*.

a)

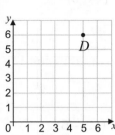

b)

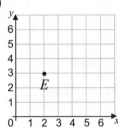

c)

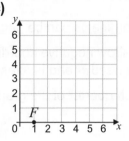

3 Find the coordinates of each point shown on the grid.

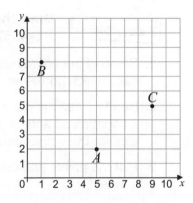

Example 2	**Draw the triangle *PQR* with corners at *P*(5, 8), *Q*(7, 0) and *R*(1, 3).**

1. Start by plotting point *P*.
   Read along the horizontal axis until you get to the correct *x*-coordinate: 5.

   Read up the vertical axis until you get to the correct *y*-coordinate: 8.

2. Repeat for points *Q* and *R* and connect the points to draw the triangle.

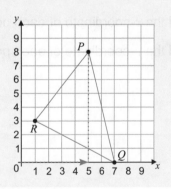

4 For each set of coordinates,
    i) plot the points and join them together on a copy of the grid shown.
    ii) name the shape you have drawn.

a) *A*(1, 3), *B*(1, 5), *C*(6, 5), *D*(6, 3)

b) *E*(1, 1), *F*(1, 6), *G*(5, 1)

c) *H*(0, 5), *I*(4, 5), *J*(4, 1), *K*(0, 1)

d) *L*(2, 1), *M*(1, 4), *N*(3, 6), *O*(5, 4), *P*(4, 1)

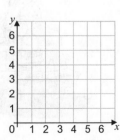

Coordinates in Four Quadrants

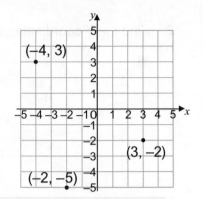

Coordinates can be negative as well as positive.

To show negative coordinates,
you need x- and y- axes in a 'cross', like this.

Each quarter of the graph is called a quadrant.

Example 3 | Draw the shape *WXYZ* with corners at *W*(−4, 5), *X*(3, 2), *Y*(4, −3) and *Z*(−5, −2).

1. Some of the coordinates are negative, so draw axes which go below zero.

2. Read across the horizontal axis for the x-coordinates and up and down the vertical axis for the y-coordinates.

3. Plot the points and connect them to draw the shape.

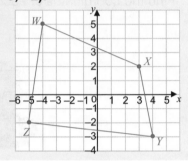

Exercise 2

1 **a)** Find the x-coordinate of each point *A-D*.

  b) Find the y-coordinate of each point *A-D*.

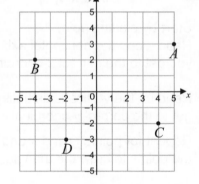

2 Find the coordinates of points *A-H* shown on the grid.

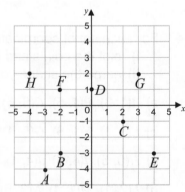

3 Match the coordinates to letters on the grid.
This should spell out the names of three shapes
when you write the letters in order.

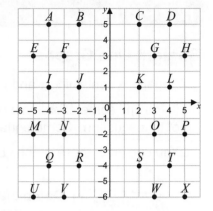

a) (2, −4) (−4, −4) (−5, −6) (−4, 5) (−2, −4) (−5, 3)

b) (2, 5) (−4, 1) (−2, −4) (2, 5) (4, 1) (−5, 3)

c) (2, 5) (−5, −6) (−2, 5) (3, −2) (−4, 1) (4, 5)

4 Draw a coordinate grid with x-values from −5 to 5
and y-values from −5 to 5.
Plot the following points on your grid,
then join the points you have plotted.

$A(3, -4)$, $B(-4, -3)$ $C(-3, 4)$ $D(2, 3)$

5 **a)** Draw a coordinate grid with x-values from −5 to 5
and y-values from −5 to 5. Plot the following points
on your grid. Join the points you have plotted.

$I(0, 4)$ $J(3, 2)$ $K(3, -2)$

$L(0, -4)$ $M(-3, -2)$ $N(-3, 2)$

b) What is the name of the shape you have drawn?

Investigate — Coordinate Maze

a) Find your way through this maze.
How could you describe your
path through the maze just using
coordinates?

b) Try designing your own maze on a four
quadrant coordinate grid like this one,
and write down a list of coordinates
which would help someone find their
way through the maze.

c) How could you make the maze harder
to solve? How could you write the
coordinates if the path didn't go
through an exact point?

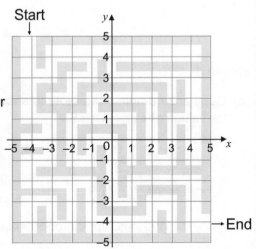

12.2 Plotting Graphs

Straight Line Graphs

Equations containing x and y describe a connection between x- and y- coordinates.

If you find some coordinate pairs that fit the equation and join them up, you get the graph of that equation. Some equations produce straight line graphs when you do this.

You can draw these graphs by filling in a table of values and plotting points.

 Complete the table to show the values of y when $y = x + 3$ and x has values from –4 to 4. Use your table to draw the graph of $y = x + 3$ for values of x from –4 to 4.

1. $y = x + 3$, so add 3 to each x-value to fill in the second row of the table.

2. Use the numbers from the first and second rows to fill in the third row.

x	–4	–3	–2	–1	0	1	2	3	4
y	–1	0	1	2	3	4	5	6	7
Coordinates	(–4, –1)	(–3, 0)	(–2, 1)	(–1,2)	(0, 3)	(1, 4)	(2, 5)	(3, 6)	(4, 7)

3. Plot the coordinates from your table on a grid and join them up to draw the graph.

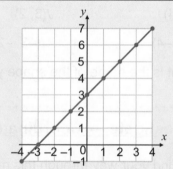

Exercise 1

1 **a)** Copy and complete the table to show the value of $y = x + 4$ for values of x from 0 to 5.

x	0	1	2	3	4	5
y	4	5				
Coordinates	(0, 4)					

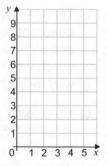

b) Copy the grid and plot the coordinates from your table.

c) Join up the points to draw the graph of the line $y = x + 4$ for values of x from 0 to 5.

2 a) Copy and complete the table to show the value of $y = 2x$ for values of x from 0 to 5.

x	0	1	2	3	4	5
y	0	2				
Coordinates	(0, 0)					

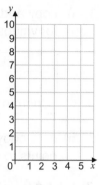

b) Copy the grid and plot the coordinates from your table.

c) Join up the points to draw the graph of the line $y = 2x$
for values of x from 0 to 5.

3 a) Copy and complete the table to show the value of $y = x - 1$ for values of x from 1 to 5.

x	1	2	3	4	5
y	0	1			
Coordinates	(1, 0)				

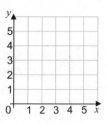

b) Copy the grid and plot the coordinates from your table.

c) Join up the points to draw the graph of the line $y = x - 1$
for values of x from 1 to 5.

4 a) Copy and complete the table to show the
value of $y = 5 - x$ for values of x from 0 to 5.

x	0	1	2	3	4	5
y	5	4				
Coordinates	(0, 5)					

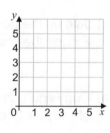

b) Copy the grid and plot the coordinates from your table.

c) Join up the points to draw the graph of the line $y = 5 - x$ for values of x from 0 to 5.

5 a) Copy and complete the table to show the value of $y = -x$ for values of x from 0 to 5.

x	0	1	2	3	4	5
y	0	−1				
Coordinates	(0, 0)					

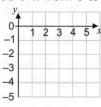

b) Copy the grid and plot the coordinates from your table.

c) Join up the points to draw the graph of the line $y = -x$
for values of x from 0 to 5.

6 For each of the following equations:

   i) copy and complete the table to show the values of y
   for values of x from −1 to 2.

x	−1	0	1	2
y				
Coordinates				

   ii) on a copy of the grid, plot the points from your table and use these
   points to draw a graph of the equation for values of x from −1 to 2.

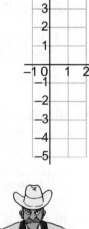

a) $y = x + 6$ **b)** $y = x - 2$ **c)** $y = x + 2$

d) $y = x - 4$ **e)** $y = x - 3$ **f)** $y = x$

7 **a)** Copy and complete the table to show the value of
   $y = 3x$ for values of x from 0 to 4.

x	0	1	2	3	4
y	0	3			
Coordinates	(0, 0)				

b) Draw a set of axes with x-values from 0 to 5 and
   y-values from 0 to 15 and plot the coordinates from your table.

c) Join up the points to draw the graph of the line $y = 3x$ for values of x from 0 to 4.
   Extend the line to show the graph of $y = 3x$ for values of x from 0 to 5.

8 **a)** Copy and complete the table to show the value
   of $y = 3x + 2$ for values of x from 0 to 3.

x	0	1	2	3
$3x$	0			
$3x + 2$	2			
Coordinates	(0, 2)			

b) Copy the grid and plot the coordinates from your table.

c) Join up the points and extend the line to draw the
   graph of $y = 3x + 2$ for values of x from 0 to 5.

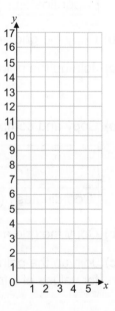

12.3 Interpreting Graphs

Horizontal and Vertical Lines

You can work out the features of <u>straight line graphs</u> just by looking at their <u>equations</u>.

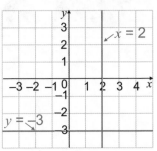

<u>Horizontal</u> lines have equations: **y = a number**.
They are <u>parallel</u> to the <u>x-axis</u>.
For example, $y = -3$ is horizontal, with all the y-coordinates at -3.

<u>Vertical</u> lines have equations: **x = a number**.
They are <u>parallel</u> to the <u>y-axis</u>.
For example, $x = 2$ is vertical, with all the x-coordinates at 2.

Exercise 1

1 a) Give the letter (A-E) of the graph that matches each of these equations:

    i) $x = 2$ **ii)** $y = 2$

    iii) $x = -6$ **iv)** $y = -6$

b) Give the equation of the remaining unmatched graph.

c) What is the equation of:

    i) the x-axis?

    ii) the y-axis?

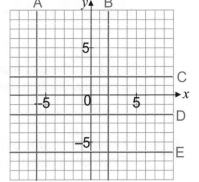

2 Draw a coordinate grid with x-values from -5 to 5 and y-values from -5 to 5, as shown.

a) Draw the graph of the horizontal line which passes through the point $(0, -4)$.

b) Copy and complete the equation of this line: $y = \boxed{}$

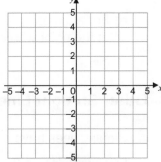

3 Draw a coordinate grid with x-values from -5 to 5 and y-values from -5 to 5.

a) Draw the graph of the vertical line which passes through the point $(2, 0)$.

b) What is the equation of this line?

4 Draw a coordinate grid with x-values from −5 to 5 and y-values from −5 to 5.
Draw the graphs of the lines with the following equations, and label them **a)-f)**.

a) $x = 1$ **b)** $x = 3$ **c)** $x = -4$

d) $y = 4$ **e)** $y = -4$ **f)** $y = -3$

5 Write down the equation of the horizontal line
which passes through the point (0, 7).

6 Write down the equation of the vertical line
which passes through the point (−3, 0).

7 Write down the equation of the line which is parallel to the y-axis
and passes through the point (2, 2).

8 Write down the equation of the line which is parallel to the x-axis
and passes through the point (−6, 4).

9 **a)** Draw the graphs of the lines with the following equations.
Draw each pair of lines on a separate set of axes.

i) $x = -3$ and $y = 1$ **ii)** $y = 4$ and $x = 5$ **iii)** $y = -2$ and $x = 3$

iv) $y = 1$ and $x = 1$ **v)** $x = -4$ and $y = -3$ **vi)** $x = 4$ and $y = -3$

b) For each pair of lines in part **a)**, write down the coordinates
of the point where they cross.

Other Straight Line Graphs

Sloping lines have equations containing both y and x.

For example, $y = 2x - 1$ and $y = 3x - 1$ are sloping.

The bigger the number before the x,
the steeper the slope. ($y = x$ means $y = 1x$.)

The other number tells you where the line crosses the y-axis.

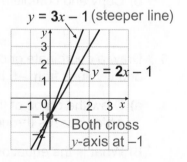

$y = 3x - 1$ (steeper line)

$y = 2x - 1$

Both cross
y-axis at −1

Exercise 2

1 Give the letter (A-C) of the line that matches each
equation. The line $y = x$ is labelled to help you.

a) $y = 2x$

b) $y = x + 5$

c) $y = x - 5$

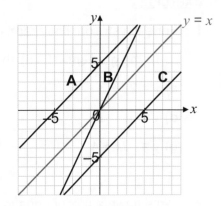

2 a) Give the letter (A-E) of the line that matches each equation.
The line $y = x$ is labelled to help you.

   i) $y = x + 3$

   ii) $y = 3x + 1$

   iii) $y = x - 8$

   iv) $y = 3x - 8$

b) Give the equation of the
remaining unmatched line.

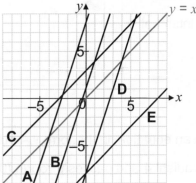

Equations of straight lines can be written in the form: $y = mx + c$.
m and **c** are numbers, where:

• **m** is the steepness or <u>gradient</u> of the line, and
• **c** tells you the <u>y-intercept</u> — the point where the line crosses the y-axis.

If c is zero (so the equation is $y = mx$) then the graph goes through the <u>origin</u>, (0, 0).
If m is zero (equation $y = c$) then the graph is a <u>horizontal</u> line through c on the y-axis.

Example 1   **A straight line has a gradient of 2 and passes
through the point (0, –1).**

**Give the equation of this straight line graph
in the form $y = mx + c$.**

1. First find m — this is the gradient. $m = 2$

2. Now find the y-intercept, c.
   The line passes through the point $c = -1$
   (0, –1) which is –1 on the y-axis.

3. Put m and c into the equation. $y = 2x + (-1)$ or $y = 2x - 1$

Exercise 3

1 For each straight line graph given by these equations, write down:

    i) the gradient,   **ii)** the coordinates of the y-intercept.

a) $y = 2x + 3$ **b)** $y = 6x + 1$ **c)** $y = 3x - 4$

d) $y = 5x$ **e)** $y = x + 7$ **f)** $y = x - 2$

g) $y = -2x + 4$ **h)** $y = 4 - 2x$ **i)** $y = 6$

2 Write down a pair of equations from the box whose graphs have the same:

a) gradient.

b) y-intercept.

$y = 2x + 2$	$y = 1 - 3x$	$y = 2 + 3x$
$y = x - 2$		$y = -3$
$y = -x - 1$	$y = -2x$	$y = 3 + x$

3 Give an equation, in the form $y = mx + c$, of a graph that has:

a) gradient 4 and passes through (0, 1).

b) gradient 2 and passes through (0, –3).

c) gradient –2 and passes through (0, 5).

d) gradient 1 and passes through the origin.

Investigate — Real Life Graphs

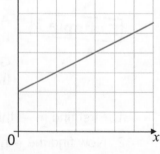

This graph shows the cost of hiring a boat for a certain number of hours. The cost includes a deposit.

a) What should the y-axis be labelled?
What about the x-axis?

b) What does the y-intercept tell you?
What about the gradient?

c) What other real life graphs might look similar to this one?
Think about what the y-intercept and gradient tell you for each one.

Section 13 — Angles and Shapes

13.1 2D Shapes

Symmetry

A <u>line of symmetry</u> is a <u>mirror line</u>, along which you can fold a shape so that both halves match up exactly. Either side of the line of symmetry is a <u>reflection</u> of the other.

Line of symmetry

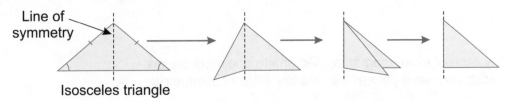

Isosceles triangle

Example 1   Draw the lines of symmetry on a square.

There are four ways you can fold this shape so that both halves match up exactly. The lines of symmetry are the fold lines.

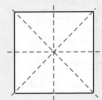

A square has **4** lines of symmetry.

Exercise 1

1 Trace each of these shapes and draw on the lines of symmetry (if there are any). State the number of lines of symmetry each shape has.

a)
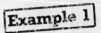

b)

c)

d)

e)

f)

2 Trace each of these shapes and draw on the lines of symmetry.
State the number of lines of symmetry each shape has.

a)

b)

c)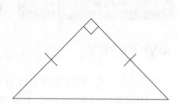

3 Copy each of these diagrams, then shade one more square
on each to make a pattern with exactly 1 line of symmetry.

a)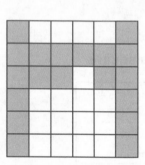

b)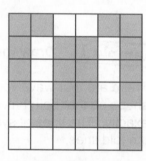

c)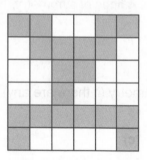

d)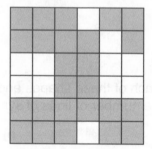

4 Copy the diagram, then shade four more squares
to make a pattern with exactly 2 lines of symmetry.

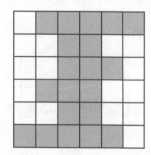

The <u>order of rotational symmetry</u> of a shape is the number of positions you can rotate the shape into so that it looks exactly the same.

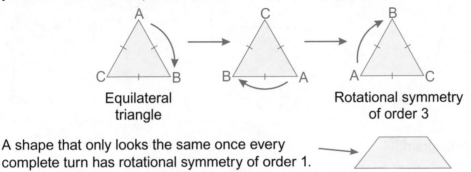

Equilateral triangle

Rotational symmetry of order 3

A shape that only looks the same once every complete turn has rotational symmetry of order 1.

Example 2 **What is the order of rotational symmetry of a square?**

There are four positions in which a square looks exactly the same.

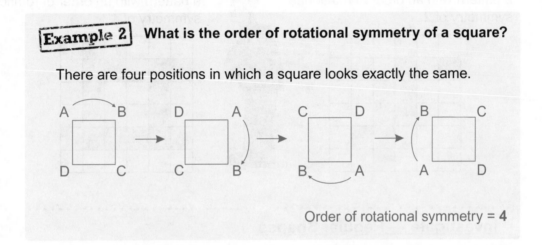

Order of rotational symmetry = **4**

Exercise 2

1   What is the order of rotational symmetry of each of these shapes?

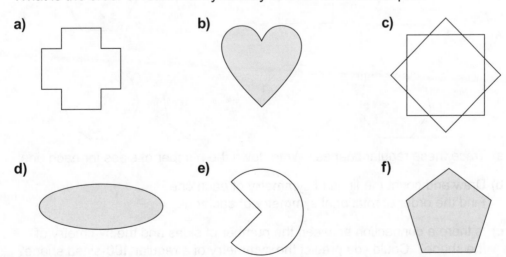

a)

b)

c)

d)

e)

f)

2   What is the order of rotational symmetry of each of these shapes?

a)

b)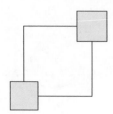

c)

3   Copy each diagram.

a) Shade one more square to make a pattern with an order of rotational symmetry of 2.

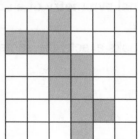

b) Shade two more squares to make a pattern with an order of rotational symmetry of 4.

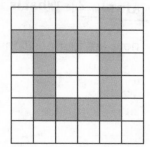

Investigate — Regular Shapes

Regular shapes have all their sides the same length and the angles the same size. A square is a regular 4-sided shape.

a) Trace these regular shapes. Write down the number of sides for each one.

b) Draw and count the lines of symmetry of each one.
   Find the order of rotational symmetry of each one.

c) Is there a connection between the number of sides and the symmetry of the shape? Could you predict the symmetry of a regular 100-sided shape?

Properties of Triangles

Triangles are three-sided shapes.

You need to know the different types of triangles and their properties.

   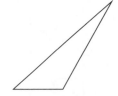

Equilateral triangle
3 equal sides
3 equal angles of 60°
3 lines of symmetry
Rotational symmetry
of order 3

Isosceles triangle
2 equal sides
2 equal angles
1 line of symmetry
Rotational symmetry
of order 1

Right-angled triangle
1 right angle (90°)
Rotational symmetry
of order 1

Scalene triangle
All sides different and
all angles different.
No lines of symmetry
Rotational symmetry
of order 1

Exercise 3

1 Write down the type of each of these triangles.

a)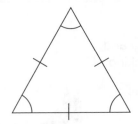

b)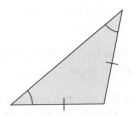

c)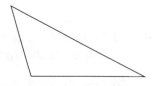

2 For each set of points,

i) copy the grid and plot the points to draw a triangle

ii) write the down the type of the triangle you've drawn

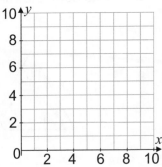

a) $J(2, 3)$, $K(5, 3)$, $L(5, 8)$

b) $R(6, 1)$, $S(3, 9)$, $T(9, 9)$

c) $X(1, 5)$, $Y(4, 4)$, $Z(3, 8)$

3 Copy and complete this table.

Sketch	Name of triangle	Number of lines of symmetry	Order of rotational symmetry
	Scalene		
		3	
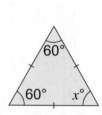			

4 a) I am thinking of a triangle. It has two angles the same size and two sides the same length. What type of triangle am I thinking of?

b) I am thinking of a triangle. All the angles are different sizes. What **two** types of triangle could I be thinking of?

5 Write down the values of x, y, z and r in these triangles.

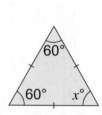
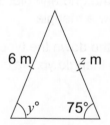

6 Trey and Lisa are looking at the same triangle. Trey says, "this triangle is isosceles". Lisa says, "this is a right-angled triangle". Can they both be correct? Explain your answer.

Properties of Quadrilaterals

Quadrilaterals are four-sided shapes.

You need to know the different types of quadrilaterals and their properties.

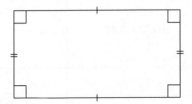

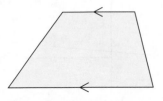

Square
4 equal sides
4 right angles (90°)
4 lines of symmetry
Rotational symmetry
of order 4

Rectangle
2 pairs of equal sides
(opposite sides are equal)
4 right angles (90°)
2 lines of symmetry
Rotational symmetry
of order 2

Trapezium
1 pair of parallel sides
Rotational symmetry
of order 1

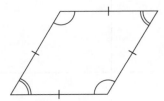

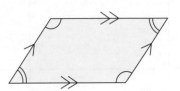

Rhombus
4 equal sides
(opposite sides are parallel)
2 pairs of equal angles
2 lines of symmetry
Rotational symmetry
of order 2

Parallelogram
2 pairs of equal sides
(opposite sides are
equal and parallel)
2 pairs of equal angles
No lines of symmetry
Rotational symmetry
of order 2

Kite
2 pairs of equal sides
1 pair of equal angles
1 line of symmetry
Rotational symmetry
of order 1

Exercise 4

1   Write down the type of each of these quadrilaterals.

a)

b)

c)

d)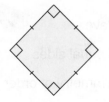

e)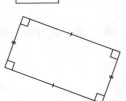

f)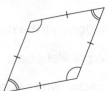

2 Copy and complete this table.

Sketch	Name of quadrilateral	Number of lines of symmetry	Order of rotational symmetry
	Trapezium		
		4	
		1	
	Rhombus		

3 Write down the values of a, b, and c in these quadrilaterals.

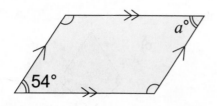

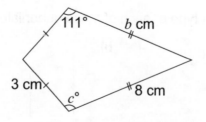

4 Write down all the different special types of quadrilateral which have:

a) no parallel sides

b) two pairs of equal sides

c) exactly two lines of symmetry

d) rotational symmetry of order 2

13.2 Properties of 3D Shapes

Here are the 3D shapes you need to know:

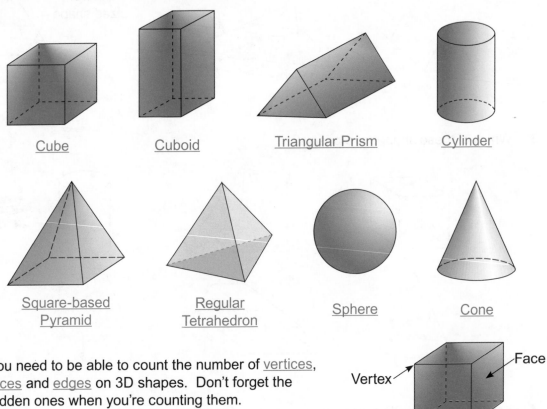

Cube   Cuboid   Triangular Prism   Cylinder

Square-based Pyramid   Regular Tetrahedron   Sphere   Cone

You need to be able to count the number of vertices, faces and edges on 3D shapes. Don't forget the hidden ones when you're counting them.

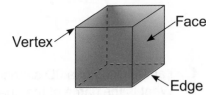

Vertex   Face   Edge

Exercise 1

1   For each of the following shapes, write down the number of: **i)** faces
                                                              ii) vertices
                                                              iii) edges

    a) Cube   **b)** Square-based pyramid   **c)** Triangular prism

2   Write down all the different types of 3D shape which have:

    a) at least one triangular face   **b)** four or fewer faces

    c) exactly twelve edges   **d)** no edges

A <u>prism</u> is a 3D shape which is the same shape and size all the way through.

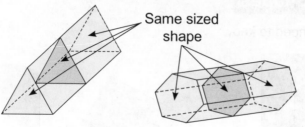

Same sized shape

This is **not** a prism: Different sized shape

3   Which of these shapes are prisms?

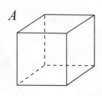
A

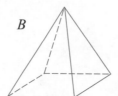
B

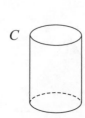
C

D

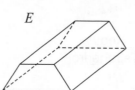
E

F

4   I am thinking of a 3D shape. It has 4 faces, 4 vertices and 6 edges.
What is the name of the shape I am thinking of?

5   Sketch a prism which has this face all the way through. ⟶
Use your sketch to write down how many
faces, vertices and edges the prism has.

> ### <u>Investigate — Making Cubes</u>
>
> *A net is a flat shape that you can fold up to make a 3D shape.*
> *A net of a cube is shown here:*
>
> **a)** How many other ways can you arrange the squares
>   of this net so it still folds up to make a cube?
>
> **b)** Cut out your nets and try folding them up into cubes.
>   Start with the one shown. Which edges join together on each net?
>   Label the pairs of edges that join together with matching letters.

13.3 Angle Rules

Angles at a Point

Angles on a straight line add up to 180°.

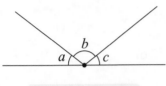

$a + b + c = 180°$

Angles around a point add up to 360°.

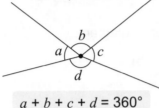

$a + b + c + d = 360°$

Angles within a <u>right angle</u> add up to 90°.

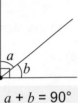

$a + b = 90°$

Example 1 Find the size of angle x.

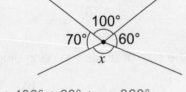

1. Use the fact that angles around a point add up to 360° to write an equation involving x.

2. Simplify the equation.

3. Solve the equation to find x.

$70° + 100° + 60° + x = 360°$

$230° + x = 360°$

$x = 360° - 230°$

$x = \mathbf{130°}$

Exercise 1

The diagrams in this exercise are **not** drawn accurately, so don't try to measure the angles.

1 Copy and complete the working to find the missing angles.

a)

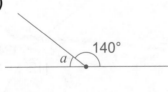

$a = 180° - ..... = ...$

b)

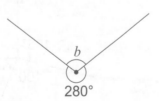

$b = ... - 280° = ...$

c)

$c = ... - ..... = ...$

2 Find the size of angle x in each diagram.

a)

b)

c)

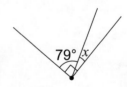

3 Find the size of angle u in each diagram.

a)

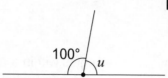

b)

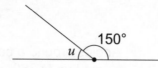

c)

4 Find the size of angle a in each diagram.

a)

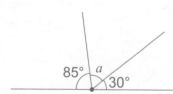

b)

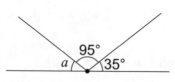

c)

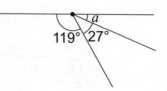

5 Find the size of angle z in each diagram.

a)

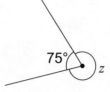

b)

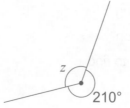

c)

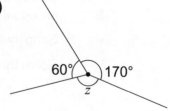

6 Find the size of angle w in each diagram.

a)

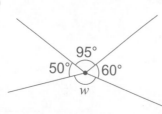

b)

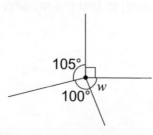

c)

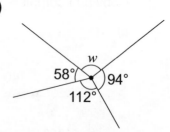

7 Which pairs of angles add up to 180° in this diagram?

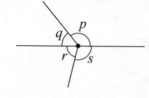

Angles around Intersecting Lines

Intersecting lines are lines that cross at a point.
At this point, opposite angles are equal —
they're known as vertically opposite angles.

Because they're angles on a straight line, $a + b = 180°$.

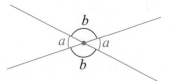

Example 2 | **Find the size of angles x, y and z shown in the diagram.**

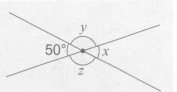

1. x and the 50° angle are vertically opposite, so they are equal.

   $x = 50°$

2. y and the 50° angle are on a straight line, so they add up to 180°.

   $y + 50° = 180°$
   $y = 180° - 50° = 130°$

3. y and z are vertically opposite, so they are equal.

   $z = y = 130°$

Exercise 2

The diagrams in this exercise are **not** drawn accurately, so don't try to measure the angles.

1 In each diagram, write down the pairs of angles which are vertically opposite.

a)

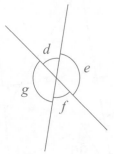

b)

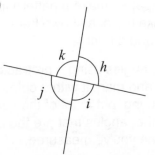

c)

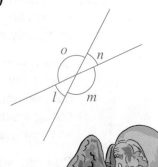

2 Write down the size of the missing angles marked by letters.

a)

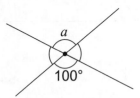

b)

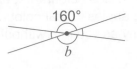

c)

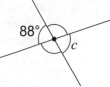

3   Find the size of the missing angles marked by letters.

a)
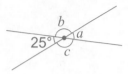

b)
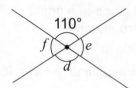

c)
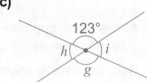

d)
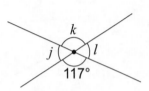

e)
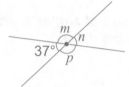

f)
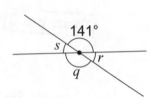

4   On a plain piece of paper, draw a line with a ruler. Using a protractor, draw a line that crosses the first one at an angle of 65°. Without measuring, label the other three angles with their correct size.

Investigate — Angle Art

a) On a plain piece of paper, make a pattern from intersecting lines (like the one shown here) using only a pencil and a ruler.

b) Measure one of the angles using a protractor, label it with its size and mark it with a coloured dot. Without measuring, put a dot of the same colour inside any other angles that are the same size as the one you've measured.

c) Can you work out the size of any other angles using the angle laws? Whenever you work out a different sized angle, pick a colour for it and mark off any matching angles in that colour. Try to work out as many as you can without measuring.

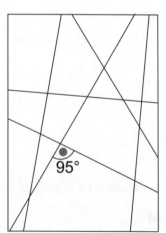

13.4 Angles in Polygons

Angles in a Triangle

The angles in a <u>triangle</u> add up to 180°. ✓

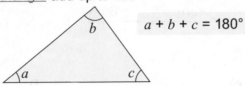

$a + b + c = 180°$

Example 1 | **Find the size of angle x.**

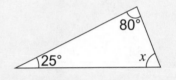

1. The angles in a triangle add up to 180°.
   Use this to write an equation involving x.

2. Solve your equation to find x.

$x + 25° + 80° = 180°$
$x + 105° = 180°$
$x = 180° - 105° = \textbf{75°}$

Exercise 1

The diagrams in this exercise are **not** drawn accurately, so don't try to measure the angles.

1 Copy and complete the working to find the missing angles.

a)

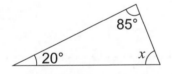

$x = 180° - 85° - ..... = ...$

b)

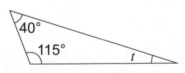

$t = ... - 115° - 40° = ...$

c)

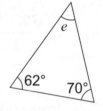

$e = 180° - ..... - ..... = ...$

d)

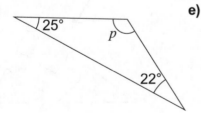

$p = ... - ..... - 22° = ...$

e)

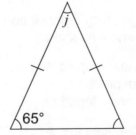

$j = 180° - ..... - ..... = ...$

f)

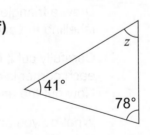

$z = ... - ..... - ..... = ...$

2 Find the size of the missing angles marked by letters.

a)

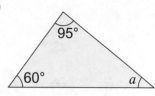

b)

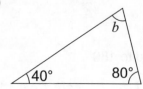

c)

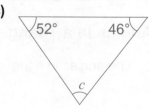

d)

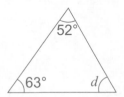

e)

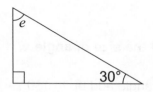

f)

3 Find the size of the missing angles marked by letters.

a)

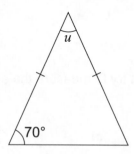

b)

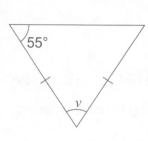

c)

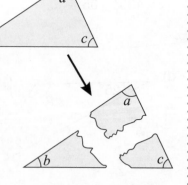

Investigate — Paper Proofs

This is a nice way of showing that the angles in a triangle add up to 180°.

Draw a triangle on a page using a pencil and ruler, labelling the angles a, b and c as shown.

Carefully cut it out, then tear it up so that each corner is a separate piece.
Now put the angles a, b and c together.

What do you notice? How does this show that $a + b + c = 180°$?

Angles in a Quadrilateral

The angles in a quadrilateral add up to 360°.

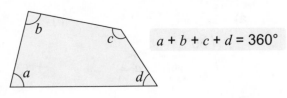

$a + b + c + d = 360°$

This is because any quadrilateral can be split into two triangles:
The angles in a triangle add up to 180°, and $2 \times 180° = 360°$.

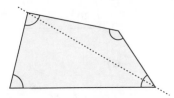

Example 2   Find the size of angle x.

1. The angles in a quadrilateral add up to 360°.
   Use this to write an equation involving x.

2. Solve your equation to find x.

$$x + 112° + 88° + 93° = 360°$$
$$x + 293° = 360°$$
$$x = 360° - 293° = \mathbf{67°}$$

Exercise 2

The diagrams in this exercise are **not** drawn accurately, so don't try to measure the angles.

1 Copy and complete the working to find the missing angles.

a)

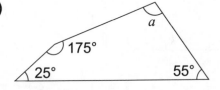

$a = 360° - 175° - 55° - ..... = ...$

b)

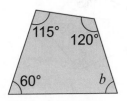

$b = ... - 120° - ..... - ..... = ...$

c)

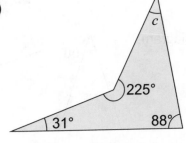

$c = 360° - ..... - ..... - ..... = ...$

d)

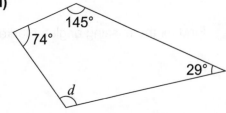

$d = ... - ..... - ..... - 29° = ...$

2 Find the size of the missing angles marked by letters.

a)
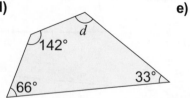

b)

c)
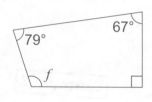

d)
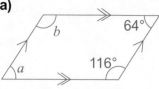

e)
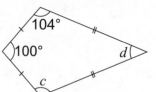

f)
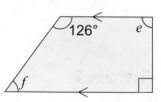

3 Use shape properties to find the size of the missing angles marked by letters.

a)

b)

c)

d)
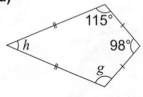

e)
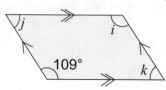

f)
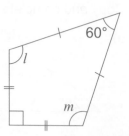

4 One angle inside a rhombus measures 27°.
Find the sizes of the other three angles.

5 Find all the missing angles marked by letters in this diagram.

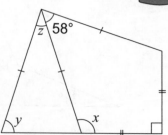

Section 14 — Constructions

14.1 Measuring and Drawing

Lines and Angles

For this topic, you'll need to use a **ruler** for measuring lengths...

...and a **protractor** for measuring angles.

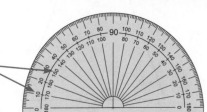

Don't get these two scales mixed up —
they start at opposite sides of the protractor
so you need to use the right one.

Angles are measured in degrees (°), for example, 90°.

Example 1	**Measure the size of angle a.**

1. Line up the 0° line of the protractor with the horizontal line.

2. Put the protractor's cross exactly where the two lines meet.

3. Read off the value where the line crosses the protractor's scale — make sure you use the correct scale. (You might have to extend the line to read off the value.)

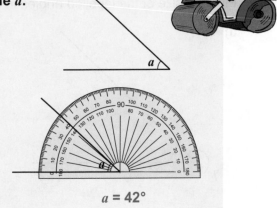

$a = 42°$

Exercise 1

In this exercise, give all answers to the nearest **whole number**.

1   In each diagram use a ruler to measure the lengths of the two sides, in mm.
    Then use a protractor to measure the size of the angle between them.

a)

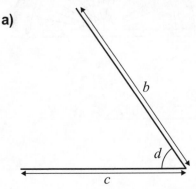

b)

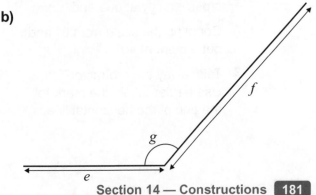

2 Give the lengths of all three sides, in mm, and the size of all three angles in each of these triangles.

a)

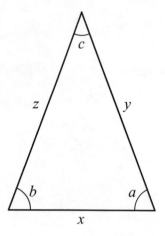

b)

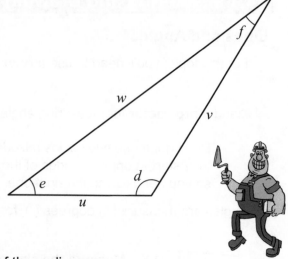

3 Find the size of the labelled angles in each of these diagrams.

a)

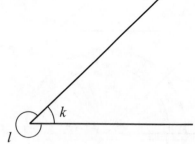

b)

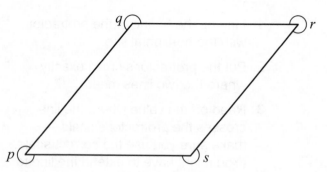

Example 2   Draw an angle of 40°.

1. Start by drawing a horizontal line.

2. Line up the 0° line of the protractor with the horizontal line and put the protractor's cross exactly at one end.

3. Count up the scale from 0° and put a mark at 40°.

4. Take away the protractor. Use a ruler to join the mark to the end of the horizontal line.

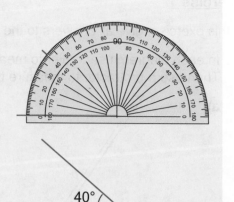

4 Use a protractor to draw angles of the following sizes.

   a) 90°   **b)** 20°   **c)** 38°

   d) 120°   **e)** 135°   **f)** 152°

5 **a)** Draw a horizontal line 9 cm long.

   b) On one end of the line, draw a line at an angle of 60° above the first line.

   c) On the other end of the line, draw a line at an angle of 45° above the first line.

6 **a)** Draw a vertical line 8 cm long and label the ends A and B.

   b) At point A, draw a 4 cm line to the right of the vertical line at an angle of 35°.

   c) At point B, draw a 3 cm line to the right of the vertical line at an angle of 68°.

7 **a)** Draw a horizontal line 5 cm long.

   b) At each end of the line, draw a 5 cm line below the horizontal line at 90° to it.

   c) Join the end points of these two lines with another horizontal line.

   d) What shape have you drawn?

8 **a)** Measure the three angles and
       the three sides of this triangle.

   b) Make an exact copy of the triangle using a
       ruler and protractor. Label the sizes of the angles
       and the lengths of the sides, in mm, on your diagram.

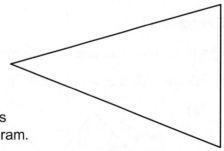

9 **a)** Find all of the angles and
       side lengths of this irregular pentagon.

   b) Make an exact copy of the irregular pentagon
       using a ruler and protractor.
       Label the sizes of the angles and the lengths
       of the sides, in mm, on your diagram.

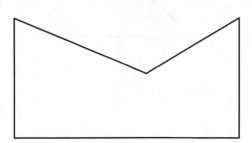

14.2 Constructing Triangles

1 Side and 2 Angles

Draw triangle *ABC*, where:
side *AB* = 5 cm, angle *ABC* = 60° and angle *BAC* = 30°.

1. Draw and label the side that
   you've been given the length of.

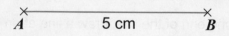

A   5 cm   *B*

2. Use a protractor to mark
   the two angles —
   ABC is at point *B* and
   BAC is at point *A*.

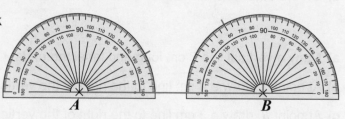

3. Draw lines from *A* and *B* to the
   angle marks and extend them.
   The point where the two lines cross is
   the third point on the triangle
   — label it *C*.

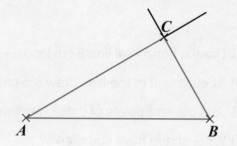

Exercise 1

The triangles in this exercise are **not** drawn to scale.

1   Draw each shape accurately and name the type of triangle you've drawn.

a)

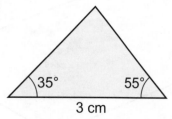

35°   55°
3 cm

b)

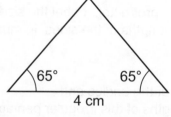

65°   65°
4 cm

c)

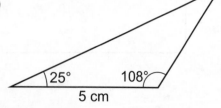

25°   108°
5 cm

d)

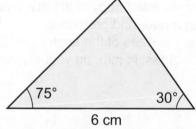

75°   30°
6 cm

2 Draw each of these triangles. Label the corners *A*, *B* and *C*.

   a) *AB* = 6 cm, angle *ABC* = 34°, angle *BAC* = 109°.

   b) *AC* = 6.5 cm, angle *ACB* = 46°, angle *BAC* = 87°.

   c) *BC* = 55 mm, angle *ABC* = 68°, angle *ACB* = 42°.

3 Draw each of these triangles accurately.
   Use a ruler to measure the lengths labelled *m* and *n* on your accurate drawings.

   a)

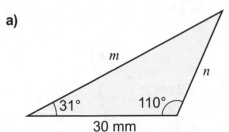

   b)

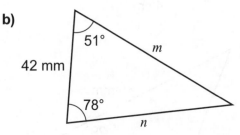

4 **a)** Draw the triangle *ABC,* where *AB* = 40 mm and angle *ABC* = angle *BAC* = 58°.

   b) Measure, in mm, the lengths of sides *AC* and *BC*.

   c) What kind of triangle have you drawn?

2 Sides and 1 Angle

Example 2 **Draw triangle *ABC*, where: side *AB* = 40 mm, side *BC* = 25 mm and angle *ABC* = 40°**

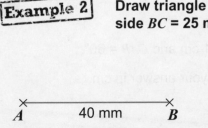

1. Draw and label one of the sides.

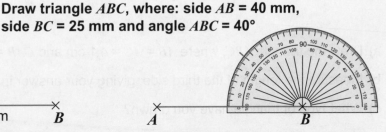

2. Mark the angle you're given.

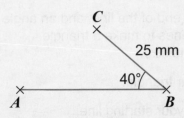

3. Draw the other side you're given using the angle you've marked.

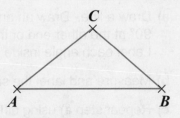

4. Draw the last line to complete the triangle.

Exercise 2

1 Draw each of these triangles accurately.
Use your drawing to find the length of the final side of the triangle, in mm.

a)

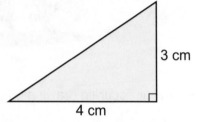

3 cm

4 cm

b)

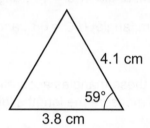

4.1 cm

59°

3.8 cm

c)

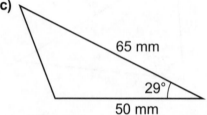

65 mm

29°

50 mm

d)

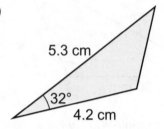

5.3 cm

32°

4.2 cm

2 Draw each of these triangles. Label the corners A, B and C.

a) AB = 8 cm, AC = 3 cm, angle BAC = 35°.

b) AC = 4.5 cm, BC = 5.3 cm, angle ACB = 71°.

c) BC = 25 mm, AB = 34 mm, angle ABC = 135°.

3 **a)** Draw the triangle ABC, where AB = AC = 4.1 cm and CAB = 60°.

b) Measure the length of the third side, giving your answer in cm.

c) What type of triangle have you drawn?

> ### Investigate — Three Angles
>
> **a)** Draw a line. Draw an angle of 30° at one end of the line, and an angle of
> 90° at the other end of the line. Join the lines to make a triangle.
> Label each angle inside the triangle with its size.
>
> **b)** Measure and label the side lengths of your triangle.
>
> **c)** Repeat step **a)** using different lengths for your starting line.
> Measure and label the side lengths of each triangle you draw.
>
> **d)** Compare the sets of side lengths for each triangle. Do you notice anything?

Section 15 — Perimeter, Area and Volume

The <u>perimeter</u> is the total distance around the outside of a shape.

Example 1 **Find the perimeter of this shape. The shape is not drawn to scale.**

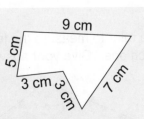

1. Put a dot on one corner of the shape.

2. Go around the shape, adding up the lengths of the sides as you go.

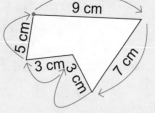

3. Stop when you get back to the dot.

4. Give your answer using the correct units. $9 + 7 + 3 + 3 + 5 = \textbf{27 cm}$

Exercise 1

The diagrams in questions 1 and 2 are **not** drawn accurately.

1 Find the perimeter of each of the following shapes.

a)

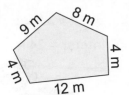

b)

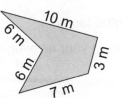

c)

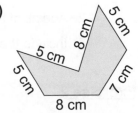

d)

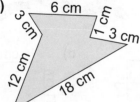

e)

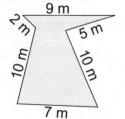

f)

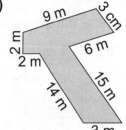

2 Find the perimeter of each of the following shapes.

a)

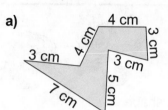

b)

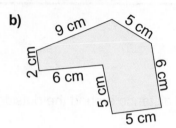

c)

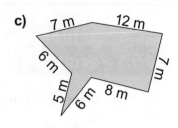

3 Use a ruler to measure the lengths of the sides of these shapes, and find the perimeter of each one. Give your answers in cm to the nearest whole number.

a)

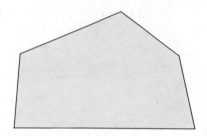

b)

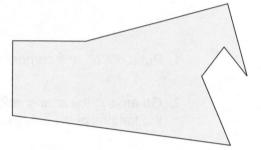

Example 2 **Find the perimeter of this rectangle.**

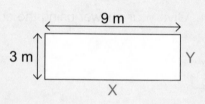

1. Start by finding the missing lengths, X and Y.
   In a rectangle, opposite sides are the same length.
   X = 9 m
   Y = 3 m

2. Add all of the side lengths together.
   9 + 3 + 9 + 3 = 24

3. Include the correct units in your answer.
   Perimeter = 24 m

Exercise 2

The diagrams in this exercise are **not** drawn accurately.

1 Work out the perimeter of each of the following squares.

a)

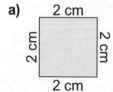

2 cm

b)

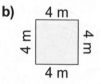

c)

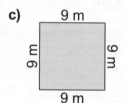

d)

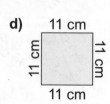

2 Work out the perimeter of each of the following rectangles.

a)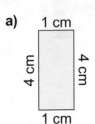
1 cm
4 cm   4 cm
1 cm

b)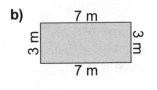
7 m
3 m   3 m
7 m

c)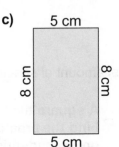
5 cm
8 cm   8 cm
5 cm

d)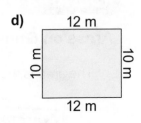
12 m
10 m   10 m
12 m

3 Work out the perimeter of each of the following squares and rectangles.

a)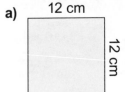
12 cm
12 cm

b)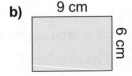
9 cm
6 cm

c)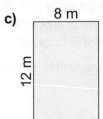
8 m
12 m

d)
10 cm
10 cm

e)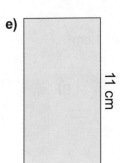
11 cm
6 cm

f)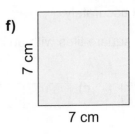
7 cm
7 cm

g)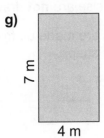
7 m
4 m

h)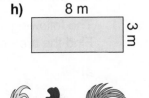
8 m
3 m

Investigate — Perimeter of Circles

A circle has no straight sides to measure, so how would you find its perimeter?

a) Use a compass to draw some circles.
Make a note of how wide you set the compass when drawing each one.
This width is called the **radius** of the circle.

b) Use a piece of string to find the distance around the outside of each circle.
This is called the **circumference** of the circle.

c) Is there any connection between the radius and the circumference of each circle? Roughly how many times bigger is the circumference than the radius?

d) Try predicting the circumference of some other circles before you draw them.

15.2 Area

Areas on Grids

The <u>area</u> is the total amount of space inside a <u>2D shape</u>.

Example 1 A square tile has an area of 1 cm².
Find the area of this shape made
up from identical square tiles.

1. Count the number of tiles in the shape.

1	2	3	4		
5	6	7	8	9	10

= 10 tiles

2. Each tile has an area of 1 cm².
So work out the area of the shape
by multiplying the number of tiles by the area of one tile.

$10 \times 1 = 10$

3. Don't forget the units. Areas always have squared units.

10 cm²

Exercise 1

The diagrams in this exercise are **not** drawn accurately.

1 The following shapes are made up from square tiles with an area of 1 cm².
Find the area of each shape.

a)   **b)** 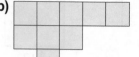   **c)** 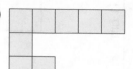   **d)**

2 Each square on these grids has an area of 2 cm². Find the area of each of the shapes.

a) 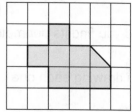   **b)** 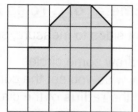   **c)**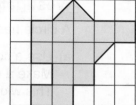

3 The grid shown is made up of squares with an area of 4 cm².
On a copy of the grid, draw a shape with an area of:

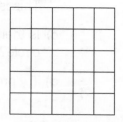

a) 20 cm²   **b)** 36 cm²   **c)** 42 cm²

Squares and Rectangles

There are formulas for finding the area of a <u>square</u> or a <u>rectangle</u>.

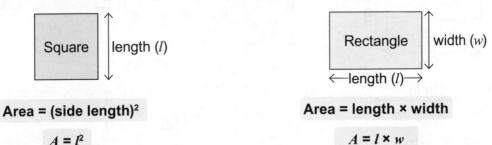

Area = (side length)²

$A = l^2$

Area = length × width

$A = l \times w$

Example 2 | **Find the area of the following shapes.**

a)

1. Write down the formula for the area of a square. $A = l^2$

2. Put the correct value for l into
   the formula and do the calculation. $A = 6^2$

3. Write your answer in the correct 'squared' units. = **36 cm²**

b)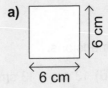

1. Write down the formula for the area of a rectangle. $A = l \times w$

2. Put the correct values for l and w into
   the formula and do the calculation. $A = 2 \times 7$

3. Write your answer in the correct 'squared' units. = **14 m²**

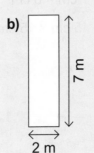

Exercise 2

The diagrams in this exercise are **not** drawn accurately.

1 Find the area of the following squares.

a)
4 cm

b)
8 m

c) 7 m

d)
11 cm

e) 9 cm

f) 5 cm

g)
2 cm

h)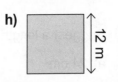
12 m

2 Find the area of the following rectangles.

a)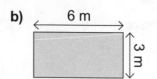
5 cm
7 cm

b) 6 m
3 m

c)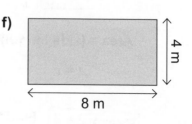
2 m
9 m

d) 11 cm
4 cm

e)
10 cm
12 cm

f)
4 m
8 m

3 Find the area of the squares and rectangles with the following dimensions.

a) 3 cm × 3 cm   b) 7 m × 4 m   c) 9 m × 1 m   d) 13 cm × 13 cm

e) 7 mm × 10 mm   f) 12 m × 8 m   g) 2 cm × 11 cm   h) 7 cm × 6 cm

i) 11 cm × 6 cm   j) 12 m × 11 m   k) 9 mm × 3 mm   l) 15 cm × 15 cm

4 A square garden has a length of 14 metres.
What is the area of the garden?

5 A swimming pool has a width of 7 metres and a length of 25 metres.
What is the area of the surface of the swimming pool?

6 Melissa paints a wall that is 5 metres high and 24 metres wide.
What is the size of the area she paints?

7 Work out the width of a square with an area of:

a) 36 cm²   b) 25 cm²   c) 81 m²   d) 4 cm²   e) 1 m²

8 Suggest a length and a width for a rectangle with the following areas.

a) 24 cm²   b) 16 cm²   c) 12 cm²   d) 30 m²   e) 42 m²

Composite Shapes

A <u>composite shape</u> is one that's made out of simpler shapes, like squares and rectangles, joined together.

To find the area of a composite shape, split the shape up into parts, find the area of each part and then add them together.

| Example 3 | Find the area of this shape. |

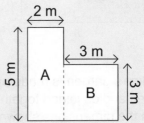

1. Split the shape up into simpler shapes —
   a rectangle (A) and a square (B).

2. Work out the area of each shape.

   $A = 2 \times 5 = 10 \text{ m}^2$
   $B = 3 \times 3 = 9 \text{ m}^2$

3. Add together the areas of A and B to
   find the total area of the shape.

   $10 + 9 = \textbf{19 m}^2$

Exercise 3

The diagrams in this exercise are **not** drawn accurately.

1 Find the area of each of the following shapes made from squares and rectangles.

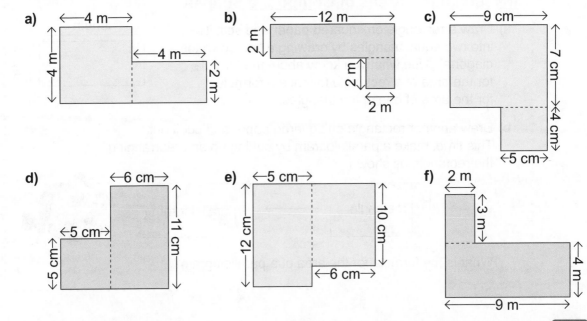

2 Find the area of each of the following shapes made from rectangles.

a)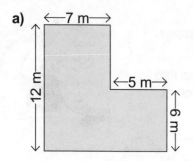

b)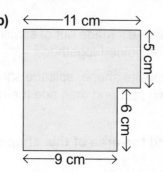

c)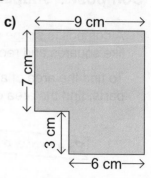

3 Caroline's garden is made up of two rectangles joined together. It has the dimensions shown in the picture. What is the area of Caroline's garden?

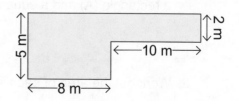

4 A car park is 70 metres long and 30 metres wide at its widest. Use this information, and the image of the car park, to work out the total area of the car park.

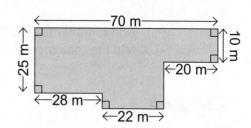

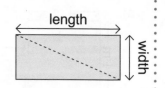

Investigate — Areas of Composite Shapes

a) Draw a rectangle on squared paper and split it into two equal triangles by drawing a line down the diagonal. Use what you know about the formula for the area of a rectangle to make a formula for the area of one of the triangles.

length

width

b) Draw another rectangle on squared paper and cut it out. This time, make a parallelogram by cutting up and rearranging the rectangle as shown:

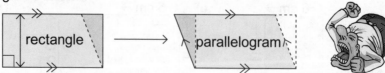

What is the formula for the area of a parallelogram?

Triangles

The <u>formula</u> for the <u>area</u> of a rectangle is **length × width**.

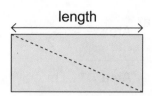

length

If you cut a rectangle in half along its diagonal,
you get two triangles that are the same size.

So the area of a triangle is half of the area of the rectangle.

The formula is: $\textbf{Area} = \dfrac{\textbf{base} \times \textbf{height}}{\textbf{2}}$ or $A = \dfrac{1}{2}bh$

The base is the length of the rectangle and the height is the width of the rectangle.

The height of the triangle in this
formula is not the sloping height.
The base and height of a triangle are
always at <u>right angles</u> to each other.

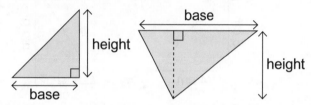

height

base

base

height

Example 4 **Calculate the area of this triangle.**

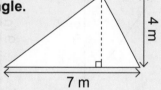

4 m

7 m

1. The base of the triangle is 7 m.
   The height of the triangle is 4 m.

2. Put these numbers into the
   formula to work out the area.

   $\text{Area} = \dfrac{\text{base} \times \text{height}}{2}$

   $= \dfrac{7 \times 4}{2}$

3. Remember to include units in your answer.
   Area is measured in square units.

   $= \textbf{14 m}^2$

Exercise 4

The diagrams in this exercise are **not** drawn accurately.

1   Copy and complete the working to find the area of each triangle.

a)
$\text{Area} = \dfrac{4 \times 6}{.....}$

$\text{Area} = \dfrac{24}{.....}$

$\text{Area} = ... \text{ cm}^2$

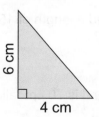

6 cm

4 cm

b)
$\text{Area} = \dfrac{5 \times .....}{2}$

$\text{Area} = \dfrac{.....}{2}$

$\text{Area} = ... \text{ cm}^2$

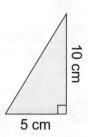

10 cm

5 cm

2 Copy and complete the working to find the area of each triangle.

a)

Area = $\dfrac{..... \times .....}{2}$

Area = ... m²

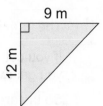

b)

Area = $\dfrac{..... \times .....}{.....}$

Area = ... m²

3 Find the area of each of these triangles.

a) 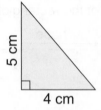 **b)** 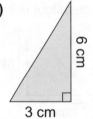 **c)** 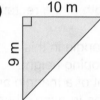 **d)**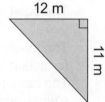

e) 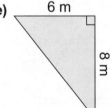 **f)** 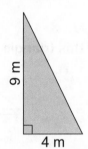 **g)** 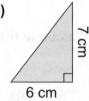 **h)**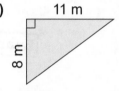

4 Find the area of each of these triangles.

a) 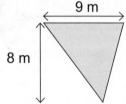 **b)** 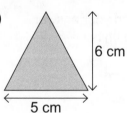 **c)** 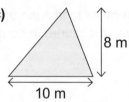 **d)**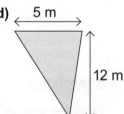

5 A triangular garden has a width of 8 metres and a length of 15 metres. What is the area of the garden?

6 A triangular mirror is 50 cm wide at the base and is 70 cm tall. What is the area of the mirror?

15.3 Volume

Cuboids

Volume (V) is the amount of space inside a 3D shape.

Example 1

A single block has a volume of 1 cm³.

Find the volume of this shape made up from identical blocks.

1. Count how many blocks there are in the shape.

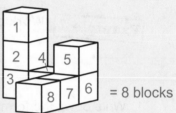

= 8 blocks

2. Each block is 1 cm³, so multiply the number of blocks by the volume of one block to find the volume of the whole shape.

$8 \times 1 = 8$

3. Give your answer with the correct units. Volume is always in cubed units.

8 cm³

Exercise 1

1 The following shapes are made from blocks with a volume of 1 cm³. Work out the total volume of each shape.

a)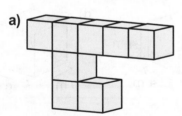

b)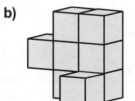

c)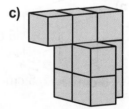

d)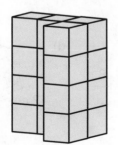

e)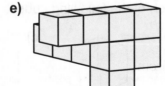

f)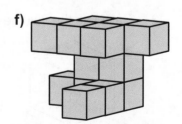

The formulas for the volume of a cube and a cuboid are:

Cube

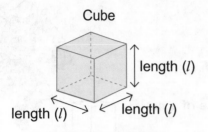

length (*l*)
length (*l*)
length (*l*)

Volume = length³

$$V = l^3$$

Cuboid

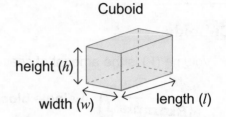

height (*h*)
width (*w*)
length (*l*)

Volume = length × width × height

$$V = l \times w \times h$$

Example 2 **Work out the volume of the cuboid.**

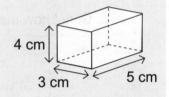

4 cm
3 cm
5 cm

1. Write down the formula for the volume of a cuboid. $V = l \times w \times h$

2. Put the correct numbers into the formula and do the calculation. $V = 5 \times 3 \times 4$

3. The answer is a volume so the units will be 'cubed'. $V = \textbf{60 cm}^3$

Exercise 2

The diagrams in this exercise are **not** drawn accurately.

1 Calculate the volume of each of the following cubes.

a)

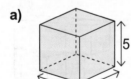

5 cm
5 cm   5 cm

b)

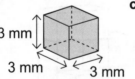

3 mm
3 mm   3 mm

c)

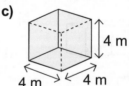

4 m
4 m   4 m

d)

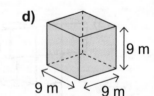

9 m
9 m   9 m

2 Calculate the volume of each of the following cubes.

a)

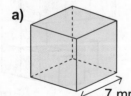

7 mm

b)

11 cm

c)

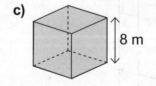

8 m

d)

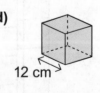

12 cm

3 Calculate the volume of each of the following cuboids.

a)
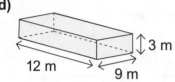
3 cm
7 cm   6 cm

b)
6 m
12 m   7 m

c)
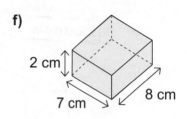
5 cm
10 cm   4 cm

d)
3 m
12 m   9 m

e)
2 mm
3 mm   9 mm

f)
2 cm
7 cm   8 cm

4 Calculate the volumes of these cubes and cuboids,
given their width (w), length (l) and height (h).

a) w = 5 cm, l = 5 cm, h = 11 cm

b) w = 12 mm, l = 12 mm, h = 11 mm

c) w = 9 m, l = 11 m, h = 7 m

d) w = 4 m, l = 11 m, h = 5 m

e) w = 3 cm, l = 11 cm, h = 12 cm

f) w = 12 cm, l = 5 cm, h = 9 cm

g) w = 12 m, l = 11 m, h = 6 m

h) w = 13 mm, l = 13 mm, h = 13 mm

5 A cuboid-shaped juice carton measures
6 cm × 6 cm × 12 cm. What is the volume
of the juice carton in cm³?

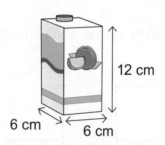
12 cm
6 cm   6 cm

6 A swimming pool is 20 metres long, 10 metres wide, and 2 metres deep.
What is the volume of the swimming pool in m³?

7 A matchbox is 60 mm long, 40 mm wide and 10 mm deep.
What is the volume of the matchbox in mm³?

8 A shoebox is 20 cm wide, 30 cm long and 15 cm deep.
What is the volume of the shoebox in cm³?

Section 16 — Transformations

16.1 Reflection

Reflection is a type of <u>transformation</u>. When an object is <u>reflected</u> in a line (called a <u>mirror line</u>), its size, shape and distance from the line stay the same.

Example 1   **Reflect this shape in the mirror line.**

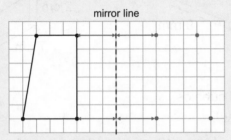
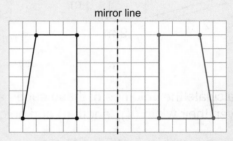

1. Reflect the points one at a time. Each reflected point should be the same distance from the mirror line as the original point.

2. Join up all of the reflected points.

Exercise 1

1   Copy these diagrams, and complete the reflection of each shape in the mirror line.

a)
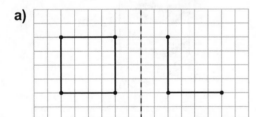

b)
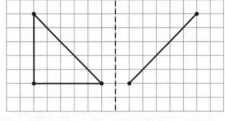

c)

d)
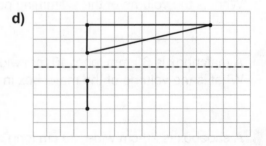

2 Copy these diagrams, and reflect each shape in the mirror line.

a)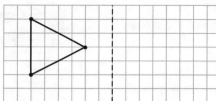

b)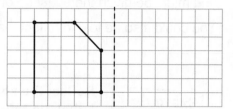

c)

d)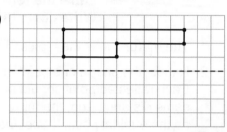

3 Copy these diagrams, and reflect each shape in the mirror line.

a)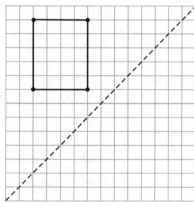

b)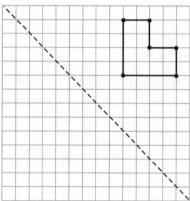

4 Copy these diagrams, and draw the mirror line that reflects one shape onto the other.

a)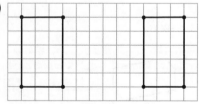

b)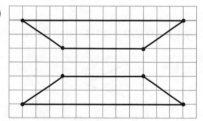

c)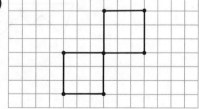

d)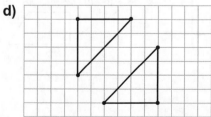

When you're reflecting shapes on a coordinate grid you might be given the equation of the mirror line.

You could also be told to reflect the shape in one of the axes.

| Example 2 | **Reflect the shape $ABCD$ in the y-axis.**
Label the reflected points A_1, B_1, C_1 and D_1.
Write down the coordinates of each reflected point. |

1. The mirror line is the y-axis.

2. Reflect the shape one point at a time. Each reflected point should be the same distance from the mirror line as the original point. Label the reflection of A with A_1, etc.

3. Write down the coordinates of each of the reflected points.

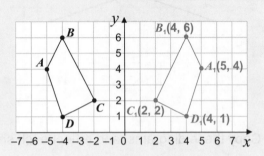

Exercise 2

1 Copy these diagrams, and reflect each shape in the y-axis.

a)

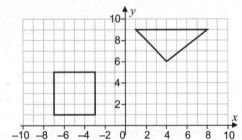

b)

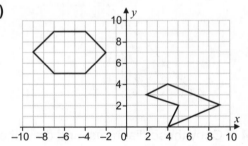

2 Copy these diagrams, and reflect each shape in the x-axis.

a)

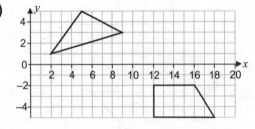

b)

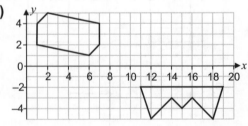

3 Copy this diagram.

   a) Reflect the shape in the y-axis.
      Label the reflection of point A with A_1.

   b) Write down the coordinates of the point A_1.

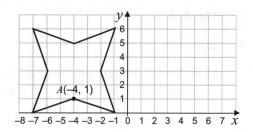

4 Copy this diagram.

   a) Reflect the shape in the y-axis
      Label the reflected points
      A_1, B_1, C_1, D_1 and E_1.

   b) Write down the coordinates of
      A_1, B_1, C_1, D_1 and E_1.

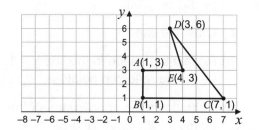

5 Copy this diagram.

   a) Reflect the shape in the x-axis.
      Label the reflected points A_1, B_1, C_1, D_1, E_1, F_1, G_1 and H_1.

   b) Write down the coordinates of
      A_1, B_1, C_1, D_1, E_1, F_1, G_1 and H_1.

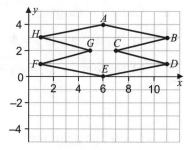

Example 3	**Reflect the shape $ABCDE$ in the line $x = 5$.**

Label the reflected points A_1, B_1, C_1, D_1 and E_1.
Write down the coordinates of each reflected point.

1. Draw the line $x = 5$. This is the vertical line passing through 5 on the x-axis.

2. Reflect the shape, one point at a time, using $x = 5$ as the mirror line.

3. Label the reflected points (so that A_1 is the reflection of A, etc.) and write down their coordinates.

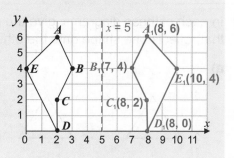

Exercise 3

1 Copy this diagram.

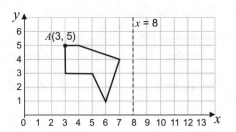

   a) Reflect the shape in the line $x = 8$.
      Label the reflection of point A with A_1.

   b) Write down the coordinates of the point A_1.

2 Copy this diagram.

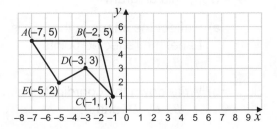

   a) Draw the line $x = 1$.

   b) Reflect the shape in the line $x = 1$.
      Label the reflected points A_1, B_1, C_1, D_1 and E_1.

   c) Write down the coordinates of the
      points A_1, B_1, C_1, D_1 and E_1.

3 Copy this diagram.

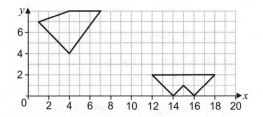

   a) Draw the line $y = 4$.

   b) Reflect the shapes in the line $y = 4$.

4 Copy this diagram.

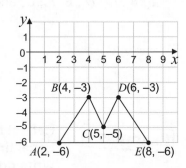

   a) Draw the line $y = -2$.

   b) Reflect the shape in the line $y = -2$.
      Label the reflected points A_1, B_1, C_1, D_1 and E_1.

   c) Write down the coordinates of
      the points A_1, B_1, C_1, D_1 and E_1.

5 In each of these diagrams, give the equation of the mirror line
that reflects one shape onto the other.

a)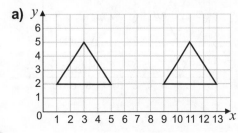

b)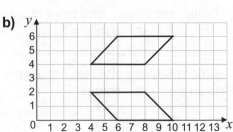

16.2 Rotation

When an object is rotated about a point, its size, shape and distance from the point of rotation all stay the same.

Rotations are described using three bits of information:

1) the centre of rotation   (the point it turns about)
2) the direction of rotation   (clockwise or anticlockwise)
3) the angle of rotation   (90°, 180° or 270°)

clockwise   anticlockwise

Example 1   **Rotate rectangle *R* 90° anticlockwise about point *T*.**

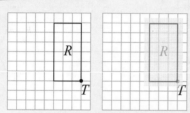
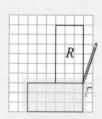
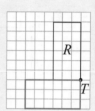

1. Draw round the shape on a piece of tracing paper.

2. Place a pencil on point *T* and rotate the tracing paper 90° (a quarter turn) anticlockwise about point *T*.

3. Draw the rectangle in its new position — point *T* will stay in the same place.

Exercise 1

1   Copy these diagrams. Rotate each shape 90° clockwise about point *T*.

a)
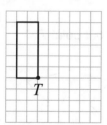

b)
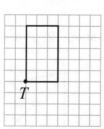

c)
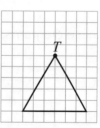

d)
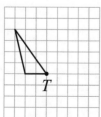

e)
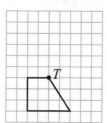

f)
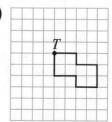

2 Copy these diagrams. Rotate each shape 90° anticlockwise about point *T*.

a)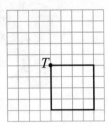

b)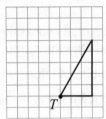

c)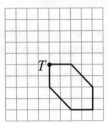

3 Copy these diagrams. Rotate each shape 180° about point *T*.

a)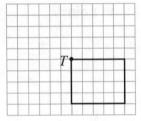

b)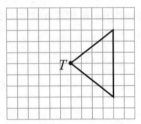

c)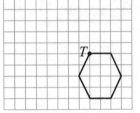

4 Copy these diagrams. Rotate each shape 270° clockwise about point *T*.

a)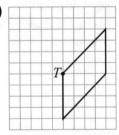

b)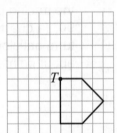

c)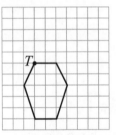

5 Copy these diagrams. Rotate each shape 270° anticlockwise about point *T*.

a)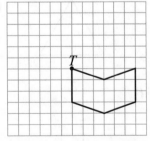

b)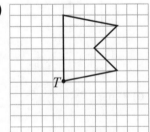

c)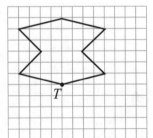

Example 2 — Rotate triangle *T* 180° about point *Q*.

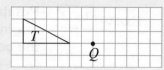

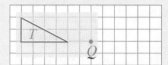

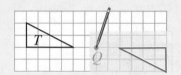

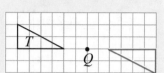

1. Draw round the shape on a piece of tracing paper.

2. Place a pencil on point *Q* and rotate the tracing paper 180° (a half turn) about point *Q*. The point *Q* doesn't move.

3. Draw the triangle in its new position.

Exercise 2

1 Copy these diagrams. Rotate each shape 180° about *P*.

a)
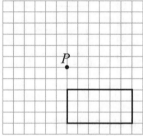

b)
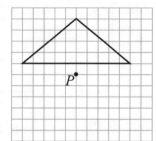

c)
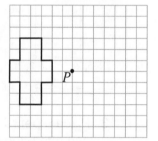

2 Copy the diagrams below. In each diagram:
i) rotate shape *A* 90° anticlockwise about *P*. Label the rotated shape *B*.
ii) rotate shape *A* 90° clockwise about point *Q*. Label the rotated shape *C*.

a)
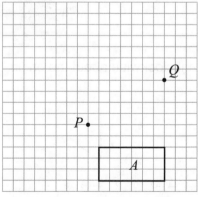

b)
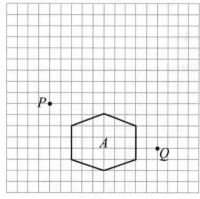

Example 3

Rotate rectangle *ABCD* **90° clockwise about the origin.** Label the rotated shape $A_1B_1C_1D_1$ and give the coordinates of each rotated point.

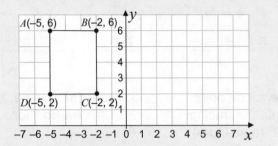

1. The origin is the point (0, 0) on the grid and 90° is a quarter turn.

2. Draw around the shape on a piece of tracing paper.

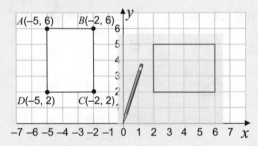

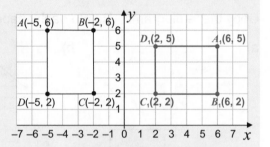

3. Place a pencil on the point (0, 0) and rotate the tracing paper 90° clockwise.

4. Draw the shape in its new position. Label the corners (so that A_1 is the rotation of point *A*, etc.) and give their coordinates.

Exercise 3

1   Copy these diagrams, and rotate each shape 90° anticlockwise about the origin.

a)
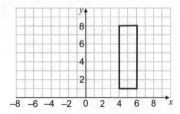

b)
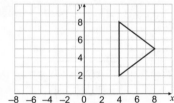

2 Copy these diagrams, and rotate each shape 180° about the origin.

a)

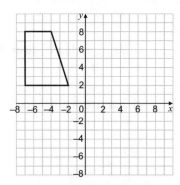

b)

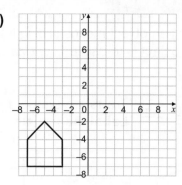

3 Copy these diagrams and rotate each shape 270° clockwise about the origin.
Label the corners of each rotated shape $A_1B_1C_1D_1E_1$.
Give the coordinates of each rotated point.

a)

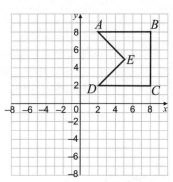

b)

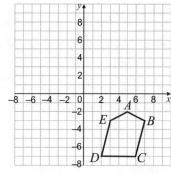

4 Copy this diagram, then:

a) rotate shape A 90° anticlockwise about (1, 3).

b) rotate shape A 90° anticlockwise about (1, 1).

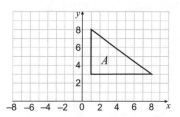

Investigate — Spot the Dot

a) Can you find the centre of rotation that takes triangle A onto triangle B?

b) Write down all the centres of rotation you can find that will take square C onto square D.

c) Investigate by drawing your own shapes on a grid and rotating them by 180°. Do any of them have more than one possible centre of rotation?

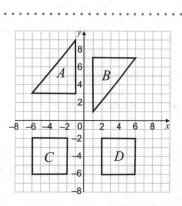

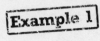

16.3 Translation

Translating an object means sliding it to somewhere else.
When an object is translated, its size and shape stay the same, but its position changes.

Example 1 | Translate shape *A* 5 squares right and 3 squares down.
Label the translated shape *B*.

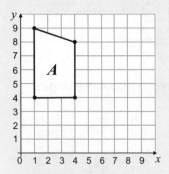 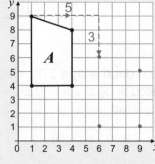 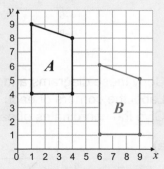

1. Translate each point one at a time.

2. Move each point 5 squares right and 3 squares down.

3. Join the translated points to make the translated shape.

Exercise 1

1 Copy these diagrams, and move each shape by the translation given.

a) 4 squares right and 2 squares up.

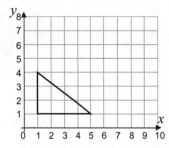

b) 5 squares left and 2 squares down.

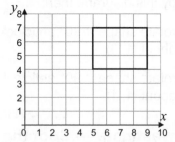

2 Copy this diagram.

a) Translate shape *A* 3 squares right and 3 squares down to give shape *B*.

b) Translate shape *A* 3 squares left and 2 squares up to give shape *C*.

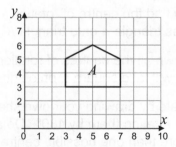

3 Copy this diagram.

   a) Translate shape P 4 squares down
   and 3 squares left to give shape P_1.

   b) Translate shape Q 3 squares up
   and 5 squares right to give shape Q_1.

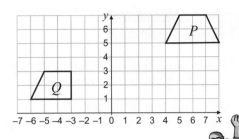

4 Copy this diagram.

   a) Translate shape R 1 square up
   and 9 squares right to give shape R_1.

   b) Translate shape S 6 squares down
   and 3 squares left to give shape S_1.

   c) Translate shape T 7 squares up
   and 2 squares right to give shape T_1.

   d) Translate shape U 2 squares up
   and 9 squares left to give shape U_1.

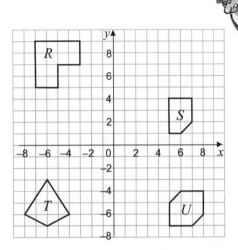

5 Describe the translation that moves shape A onto shape B in each of these diagrams.

a)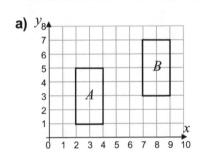

b)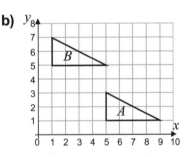

c)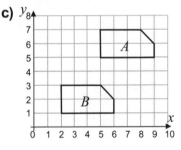

6 Use this diagram to describe the
translation that moves:

   a) shape A onto shape B

   b) shape B onto shape A

   c) shape A onto shape C

   d) shape C onto shape A

   e) shape B onto shape C

   f) shape C onto shape B.

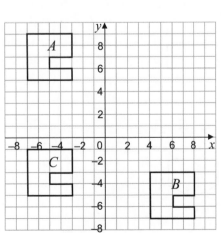

16.4 Enlargement

When an object is enlarged, its size changes but its shape stays the same.
Two objects that are the same shape but different sizes are similar.

Enlargements are described using
scale factors and centres of enlargement.

1) The scale factor tells you how the lengths of the sides change.

2) The centre of enlargement tells you where the enlargement is measured from.

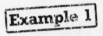

Example 1 **Enlarge this triangle by scale factor 3.**

1. Find the length of the sides for the shape you're enlarging.

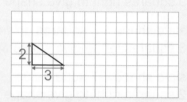

2. Multiply each side length by the scale factor to find the side lengths of the new shape.

The enlarged triangle will have:
• a base length of 3 × 3 = 9 squares
• a height of 2 × 3 = 6 squares.

3. Draw the enlarged shape using the dimensions you've found.

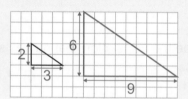

Exercise 1

1 Copy these diagrams. Enlarge each shape anywhere on the grid by scale factor 2.

a)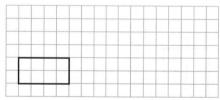

b)

c)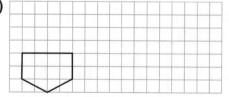

d)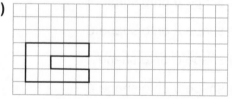

2   Copy these diagrams. Enlarge each shape anywhere on the grid by scale factor 4.

a)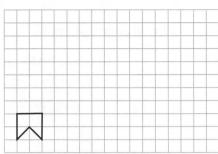

b)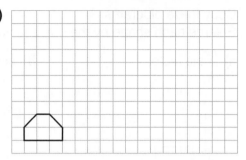

3   Draw these shapes accurately after they have been enlarged by scale factor 2.

a)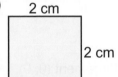

b)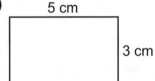

c)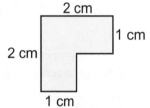

4   A regular octagon has a side length of 7 cm. What is the side length
of the octagon after an enlargement by scale factor 6?

5   An isosceles triangle has a base length of 3 cm and a height of 10 cm.
What are the base length and height of the triangle after an enlargement by scale factor 8?

Example 2   **Enlarge this rectangle by scale factor 2 with centre of enlargement (0, 0).**

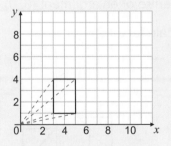

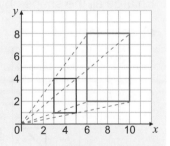

1. Draw a line from the centre of enlargement (0, 0) to each corner of the shape.

2. The scale factor is 2, so extend each line until it is 2 times as long as before.

3. Join up the ends of the extended lines to draw the enlarged shape.

Exercise 2

1 Copy these diagrams.
   Enlarge each shape by the scale factor given, with centre of enlargement (0, 0).

   a) scale factor 2   **b)** scale factor 2   **c)** scale factor 3

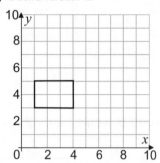   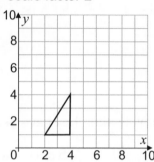   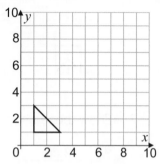

2 Copy these diagrams.
   Enlarge each shape by the scale factor given, with centre of enlargement (0, 0).

   a) scale factor 2   **b)** scale factor 3

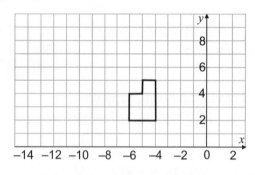   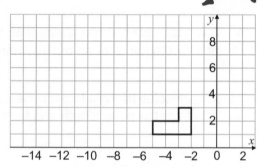

3 Copy these diagrams.
   Enlarge all the shapes by the scale factor given, with centre of enlargement (0, 0).

   a) scale factor 3   **b)** scale factor 2

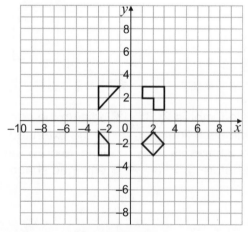   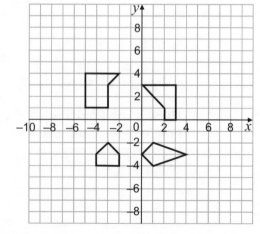

Section 17 — Probability

17.1 The Probability Scale

Probability is about how likely it is that an event will happen.

The probability will be somewhere between impossible and certain.

You can put probabilities on a scale like this:

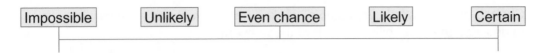

All probabilities can be written as a number between 0 (impossible) and 1 (certain).

So, using fractions, the probability scale looks like this:

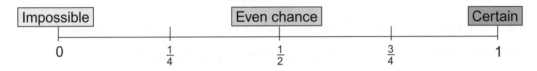

You can also write probabilities as decimals or percentages:

e.g. $\frac{1}{2}$, 0.5 and 50% are all different ways of writing 'even chance'.

Example 1   **I spin a fair, six-sided spinner numbered 1-6.**
This scale shows the probabilities of four possible
events. Match each description to the correct event.

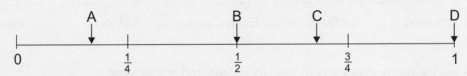

The spinner lands on an even number.

There is an equal chance of getting an even or odd number.   This describes Event B.

The spinner lands on a number that is 4 or less.

Four out of six numbers are 4 or less, so this is fairly likely.   This describes Event C.

The spinner lands on a number between 1 and 6.

All the numbers are between 1 and 6, so this is certain.   This describes Event D.

The spinner lands on a 6.

There's one 6 out of six numbers so this is quite unlikely.   This describes Event A.

Exercise 1

1   Put the events 1 to 3 in order from **least to most likely**.

    1. You will grow a third arm.

    2. You will eat something tomorrow.

    3. Someone you know will win a car this week.

2   Choose from the words *impossible*, *unlikely*, *even*, *likely* and *certain*
to describe the probability of each of these events.

    a) Rolling a fair six-sided dice numbered 1-6 once and getting a 2 and a 3.

    b) Getting a number between 1 and 8 on a spinner labelled 1, 2, 3, 4, 5, 6, 7, 8.

    c) Rolling a '1' on a fair six-sided dice numbered 1-6.

    d) Picking either a club or a diamond from a shuffled pack of playing cards.

    e) Rolling an odd number on a fair six-sided dice numbered 1-6.

    f) Spinning red on a fair spinner coloured red, yellow, red, red, blue and red.

3   This probability scale shows the probability of four events — A, B, C and D.
Match each description **a)-d)** to the correct event (A to D).

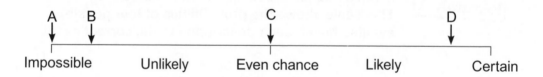

    a) It will be sunny every day in the UK in December this year.

    b) You will pick a red card from a shuffled pack of playing cards.

    c) You will go to sleep in the next 24 hours.

    d) A cat will talk to you tomorrow.

4   These eight cards are placed face down on a table and one is picked at random.

G I G G L I N G

Draw a probability scale, labelled from impossible to certain, and add arrows
to show the probability of picking each of the letters G, I, L and N.

5   A card is picked at random from a shuffled pack of 52 playing cards.

This probability scale shows the probability of four possible events.
Match each description to the correct event.

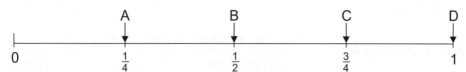

a) Picking either a red card or a black card.   **b)** Picking a card which is a club.

c) Picking a black card.   **d)** Picking a card which isn't a diamond.

6   This probability scale shows the probability of four events — A, B, C and D.
Match each description to the correct event.

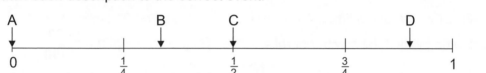

a) The next baby born in the UK being a boy.

b) Tossing a coin and getting neither head nor tails.

c) Rolling a 1 or a 2 on a fair six-sided dice numbered 1-6.

d) Getting green when you spin a fair spinner with 9 green sections and one red section.

7   Draw a probability scale from 0 to 1. Mark on the probability of these events:

a) Rolling a fair, eight-sided dice numbered 1-8 and getting a 1 or 2.

b) Rolling a fair, four-sided dice numbered 1-4 and getting a 4 or less.

c) Tossing a coin and getting heads.

Investigate — Probability Scales

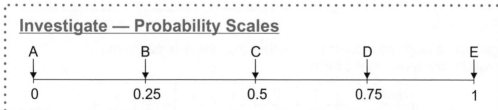

a) How many events can you write down for each of the letters A to E
on this probability scale?

b) Which letter is the hardest to think of events for? Which is the easiest?

17.2 Probability Experiments

You can <u>estimate</u> probabilities using the results of an experiment or what you know has already happened:

$$\text{Estimated probability} = \frac{\text{Number of times the result has happened}}{\text{Number of times the experiment has been carried out}}$$

Example 1

An unfair dice is rolled 100 times. The results are in the table.

Score	1	2	3	4	5	6
Frequency	14	13	26	23	13	11

Estimate the probability of rolling a 4.

1. Find the number of times 4 was rolled.   4 was rolled 23 times out of 100.

2. Divide by the total number of rolls.   So probability of a 4 = $\frac{23}{100}$

($\frac{23}{100}$ is equivalent to **23%** or **0.23**)

Exercise 1

1 Tim wants to estimate the probability that a slice of toast lands with the buttered side up when it's dropped. He drops the toast 50 times. It lands with the buttered side up 17 times. Estimate the probability, as a fraction, that the toast lands:

a) with the buttered side up,

b) with the buttered side down.

2 A spinner with four sections numbered 1-4 is spun 100 times. The results are shown in the table.

Estimate the probability of spinning each number. Give your answers as percentages.

Number	1	2	3	4
Frequency	49	34	8	9

3 Abigail rolls a dice and records the number that she gets each time. Her results are shown in the table.

Number	1	2	3	4	5	6
Frequency	26	21	18	31	19	15

Estimate the probability, as a fraction, of rolling each number.

4 Steph records the colour of socks that a group of people are wearing.
Her results are in the table.

Colour	Red	Blue	Yellow	Green	Black
Frequency	9	16	3	18	4

   a) Estimate the probability, as a simplified fraction, that someone is wearing:

     i) red socks,   **ii)** green socks.

   b) Estimate the probability that someone is not wearing red, yellow or green socks.
      Give your answer as a fraction in its simplest form.

5 25 pizzas have been topped by a random pizza-topping machine.
15 of the pizzas are topped with pepperoni.
Estimate the probability that the next pizza to come out of the
machine is topped with pepperoni. Give your answer as:

   a) a simplified fraction   **b)** a percentage   **c)** a decimal

6 A 5-sided spinner was spun 200 times with the following results.

Number	1	2	3	4	5
Frequency	46	54	38	41	21

Estimate the probability of each result as a simplified fraction,
a decimal, and a percentage.

Investigate — Rock, Paper, Scissors

In the game 'rock, paper, scissors', both players make a fist with one hand.
On the count of three, the players make either a rock (by keeping their hand in
a fist), a sheet of paper (by holding their hand out flat), or a pair of scissors (by
sticking out their first two fingers).

If both players make the same thing, it's a tie. If a rock and scissors are played,
the rock wins. If scissors and paper are played, the scissors win. If paper and a
rock are played, the paper wins.

a) Play at least 20 games of 'rock, paper, scissors' with a friend.
    Record the results as you go — write down who won, and what with.

b) After you've finished playing, organise your results into a table
    and use this to estimate some probabilities. Who was most likely to win?
    Were either of you more likely to play a certain object each time?
    Could you use this information to help you win more games next time?

17.3 Theoretical Probabilities

Calculating Probabilities

You can work out the <u>probability</u> of an <u>event</u> happening using this <u>formula</u>:

$$\text{Probability of an event} = \frac{\textbf{Number of ways the event can happen}}{\textbf{Total number of possible outcomes}}$$

You can only use this formula if each possible <u>outcome</u> is equally likely to happen — e.g. throwing a dice or picking a ball from a bag containing balls of the same size.

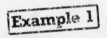 **A bag contains 5 yellow counters, 6 black counters and 4 white counters. One counter is picked at random. What is the probability that the counter is black?**

1. Find the total number of possible outcomes.

   Total number of counters = 5 + 6 + 4 = 15

2. Find the number of ways the event 'pick black' can happen.

   There are 6 black counters

3. Put the numbers into the formula and simplify.

   $$\text{Probability of picking black} = \frac{\text{number of ways of picking black}}{\text{total number of counters}}$$

   $$= \frac{6}{15} = \frac{2}{5}$$

Exercise 1

For this exercise, give each probability as a fraction in its simplest form.

1 A peg is picked at random from a bag containing 3 red pegs, 6 blue pegs and 1 green peg.

   a) What is the total number of possible outcomes?

   b) How many ways can the event 'picking blue' happen?

   c) Find the probability that a peg picked at random will be blue.

2 **a)** What is the total number of possible outcomes on this fair spinner?

   b) What is the probability of spinning:

   i) a 3?   **ii)** a 2?   **iii)** an even number?

3 A box of chocolates contains 2 milk chocolates, 7 plain chocolates and 3 white chocolates. Find the probability that a chocolate picked at random will be a white chocolate.

4 A fair, six-sided dice numbered 1-6 is rolled once.

a) Find the probability of rolling a 1.

b) How many ways can the event 'rolling a number greater than 3' happen?

c) Find the probability of rolling a number greater than 3.

5 A standard pack of 52 playing cards is shuffled and one card is selected at random. Find the probability of selecting:

a) a king

b) a black card

c) a diamond

6 A fair spinner has 16 equal sections. 4 of them are red, 3 are blue, 5 are orange and the rest are green. Find the probability that the spinner lands on:

a) red   **b)** green

c) black   **d)** any colour except red

e) blue or orange

For any event, there are only two possibilities — it either happens or it doesn't happen.

So the <u>probability</u> of an event happening and the probability of the same event not happening always add up to 1. This means that:

Probability an event doesn't happen = 1 – (Probability the same event does happen)

> 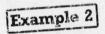 **The probability that Gemma passes her Maths test is 0.8. Find the probability that she doesn't pass her Maths test.**
>
> Gemma either passes or doesn't pass her Maths test, so:
> Probability Gemma doesn't pass = 1 – (Probability Gemma does pass)
> = 1 – 0.8
> = **0.2**

Exercise 2

1 The probability that I will receive a parcel today is 0.6.
What is the probability that I won't receive a parcel today?

2 Ben travels to work by train each day.

    a) The probability that he catches his train is 0.9.
    What is the probability that he does not catch his train?

    b) The probability of the train being late is 0.2.
    What is the probability that the train is not late?

3 The probability that a badminton player wins his game is 85%.
Find the probability, as a percentage, that he doesn't win his game.

4 The probability that it will rain tomorrow is 0.66.
What is the probability that it won't rain tomorrow?

5 I spin a fair five-sided spinner numbered 1-5.

    a) What is the probability that I get an even number? Give your answer as a fraction.

    b) What is the probability that I do not get an even number?
    Give your answer as a fraction.

6 There are 100 pupils in Year 9. 65 pupils are girls. 40 pupils wear glasses.
Find the probability that a randomly selected pupil:

    a) is a boy   **b)** doesn't wear glasses

    Give your answers as decimals, percentages and as fractions in their simplest forms.

7 A bag contains 7 red balls, 2 green balls, 3 yellow balls and 8 blue balls.
Find the probability, as a fraction, that a ball picked at random is:

    a) not red

    b) not yellow

    c) not blue or yellow

Listing Outcomes

When two <u>trials</u> are combined — for example, tossing a coin and rolling a dice — it can help to list all the possible <u>outcomes</u>.

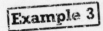 **Sarah has two standard packs of playing cards. She picks a card at random from each. Find the probability that she gets at least one red card.**

1. First draw a table to list all the possible outcomes.

Pack 1	Pack 2
red	red
red	black
black	red
black	black

2. Work out the total number of possible outcomes, and the number of ways of getting at least one red card.

   Total number of possible outcomes = 4

   Number of ways of getting at least one red card = 3

3. Work out the probability using the formula:

$$\text{Probability} = \frac{\text{number of ways of getting at least one red}}{\text{total number of possible outcomes}} = \frac{3}{4}$$

Exercise 3

1 A coin is flipped and a fair 4-sided spinner numbered 1-4 is spun.
Copy and complete the table below to list all the possible outcomes.

Coin	Heads	Heads				Tails		Tails
Spinner	1			4		2	3	

2 One card is picked at random from a standard pack of playing cards and its colour is written down. At the same time, a spinner with sections numbered 1 to 3 is spun.

Copy and complete this table to list all the possible outcomes:

Card	Red	Red				Black
Spinner		2				3

3 Elliot has two bags of sweets.
In Bag 1 there is one strawberry, one lemon and one orange sweet.
In Bag 2 there is one lime and one apple sweet.
He chooses one sweet from each bag.

a) Draw a table listing all the possible outcomes.

b) What is the total number of possible outcomes?

4 The table shows all the possible outcomes of tossing a fair coin and rolling a fair four-sided dice.

Coin	Dice
heads	1
heads	2
heads	3
heads	4
tails	1
tails	2
tails	3
tails	4

   a) What is the total number of possible outcomes?

   b) How many ways can the event "getting tails and an even number" happen?

   c) Find the probability of getting tails and an even number. Give your answer as a fraction in its simplest form.

5 A fair spinner has four sides coloured red, yellow, green and blue.

   a) Draw a table listing all the possible outcomes if this spinner is spun twice.

   b) Find the total number of possible outcomes.

   c) How many ways can the event "getting yellow at least once" happen?

   d) Find the probability of spinning the spinner twice and getting yellow at least once. Give your answer as a fraction in its simplest form.

6 A summer camp offers the activities shown here.

> *Choose 1 morning activity and 1 afternoon activity:*
>
> **Morning**   **Afternoon**
> Tennis   Hiking
> Swimming   Canoeing
> Football   Cycling

   a) Draw a table listing all the different combinations of activities available.

   Chava picks one combination at random.

   b) What is the probability, as a simplified fraction, that she chooses swimming?

   c) What is the probability, as a simplified fraction, that she chooses football and canoeing?

7 A fair four-sided spinner numbered 1-4 is spun twice.

   a) Draw a table listing all the possible outcomes.

   b) What is the probability, as a simplified fraction, of spinning a 4 on both spins?

   c) What is the probability, as a simplified fraction, of getting more than 2 on both spins?

A <u>sample space diagram</u> can be used to list all the possible <u>outcomes</u> of two <u>trials</u>. This is just a table with the outcomes of one trial down the side and the outcomes of the other trial along the top.

The sample space diagram for tossing two coins looks like this:

	Second coin	
First coin	Heads	Tails
Heads	HH	HT
Tails	TH	TT

Exercise 4

1 A coin is tossed and a fair four-sided spinner numbered 1-4 is spun.
Copy and complete the sample space diagram to show all the possible outcomes.

Spinner

	1	2	3	4
Coin Heads	H1		H3	
Tails				T4

2 A fair spinner with three equal sections of red, orange and green is spun twice.
Copy and complete the sample space diagram to show all the possible outcomes.

	Red	Orange	Green
Red			RG
Orange	OR		
Green			

3 Two fair four-sided spinners are spun and the scores added together. One is numbered 1-4 and the other is numbered 2, 4, 6 and 8.

a) Copy and complete the sample space diagram to show all the possible outcomes.

b) Find the total number of possible outcomes.

	2	4	6	8
1	3			
2			8	
3				
4		8		12

. . . .

Investigate — Picking a Winner

Two friends are playing a game where they try to predict the score when two six-sided dice are rolled and the numbers added together. If one of them guesses the score correctly, they get a point.

a) Are all the scores equally likely to come up? Or are some more likely than others? How could you work this out?

b) What score would you choose as a prediction, and why?

Section 18 — Statistics

18.1 Tables, Bar Charts and Pictograms

Frequency Tables

A frequency table shows the number of items of data that fall into certain categories. These categories can have a single description or value, or a range of values can be grouped together. Grouped frequency tables make it easier to understand large amounts of data, but they don't show the exact data values.

Example 1 The frequency table shows the number of holidays the pupils in class 7A went on in the last year.

Holidays	Frequency
0	7
1	14
2	10
3	3
4	1

a) **How many pupils are there in class 7A?**

The frequency column shows the number of pupils for each category, so add up the numbers in the frequency column.

$$7 + 14 + 10 + 3 + 1 = \mathbf{35}$$

b) **How many pupils went on 2 or more holidays?**

Add up the frequencies of all the pupils who went on 2, 3 or 4 holidays.

$$10 + 3 + 1 = \mathbf{14}$$

c) **What percentage of pupils went on 0 holidays?**

1. Find the frequency of pupils who went on 0 holidays and write this as a fraction of the total. $\frac{7}{35}$ went on 0 holidays

2. Find the percentage by dividing the top number by the bottom number and multiplying by 100. $(7 \div 35) \times 100 = \mathbf{20\%}$

Exercise 1

1   A group of people are asked which season they were born in. Their results are as follows:

spring, spring, winter, summer, summer, autumn, winter, winter, spring, autumn, summer, autumn, summer, spring, winter, winter, spring, autumn, summer, winter.

a) Copy and complete the frequency table to show these results.

Use your frequency table to answer the following questions:

b) How many people were asked?

c) How many people were born in summer or winter?

Season	Frequency
Spring	
Summer	
Autumn	
Winter	

2 The frequency table shows the hair colour of all the people on a bus.

Hair Colour	Frequency
Blonde	8
Brown	20
Red	4
Black	6
Grey	2

a) How many people are on the bus?

b) How many people have red hair?

c) How many people have blonde or brown hair?

d) What is the most common hair colour on the bus?

3 The frequency table shows the number of pets owned by the pupils in class 7B. No one had more than 5 pets.

Number of Pets	Frequency
0	6
1	7
2	4
3	4
4	3
5	1

a) How many pupils are there in class 7B?

b) How many pupils have no pets?

c) How many pupils have fewer than 3 pets?

d) What is the most common number of pets?

e) What percentage of pupils have 2 pets?

f) What percentage of pupils have more than 2 pets?

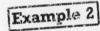 **Example 2** The grouped frequency table shows the marks the pupils in Year 8 scored in their last exam.

Exam Mark	Frequency
0-20	4
21-40	20
41-60	35
61-80	21
81-100	10

a) **How many pupils are there in Year 8?**

Add up the numbers in the frequency column.
4 + 20 + 35 + 21 + 10 = **90**

b) **How many pupils scored more than 60 marks?**

Add up the frequencies for the groups 61-80 and 81-100.
21 + 10 = **31**

c) **What is the lowest possible mark a pupil could have scored?**

The first class in the table is 0-20, so the lowest possible mark is 0. However, it's not possible to tell if anyone actually scored 0 marks as the data is grouped.   **0 marks**

Exercise 2

1 A speed camera records the speeds of some cars. The results, in mph, are as follows.

22, 25, 32, 36, 40, 42, 37, 44, 26, 29, 39, 34, 35, 30, 34, 28, 25, 48, 41, 33

a) Copy and complete the grouped frequency table to show the speeds recorded.

Use your frequency table to answer the following questions:

b) How many cars' speeds were recorded?

c) How many cars were travelling at up to 30 mph?

d) How many cars were breaking the 40 mph speed limit?

Speed (mph)	Tally	Frequency
21-25		
26-30		
31-35		
36-40		
41-45		
46-50		

2 The ages of people visiting a library one Saturday are recorded in the grouped frequency table shown.

a) How many people visited the library in total?

b) How many people were between 21 and 50?

c) What percentage of people were over 50?

d) What percentage of people were 40 or under?

Age (years)	Frequency
20 or under	30
21-30	18
31-40	12
41-50	16
51 or over	24

3 The grouped frequency table shows the number of calls a customer services helpline received each day over 20 weeks, excluding weekends.

a) On how many days did the helpline receive more than 75 calls?

b) What percentage of days did the helpline receive between 26 and 100 calls?

c) What is the most common group for the number of calls received in a day?

d) i) What is the highest possible number of calls the helpline received on one day?

ii) Explain why you can't know for certain if there was a day that the helpline received that number of calls.

Number of Calls	Frequency
0-25	5
26-50	12
51-75	23
76-100	25
101-125	22
126-150	13

Bar Charts

Bar charts (and bar-line charts) show how many items fall into different categories. The number of items in each category is the frequency.

Example 3 Will asked everyone in his class how they get to school. The bar chart shows the results.

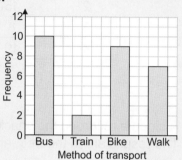

a) **What was the most popular transport?**

Look for the tallest bar. **Bus** was the most popular.

b) **How many people did Will ask?**

Add together the frequencies for each type of transport. $10 + 2 + 9 + 7$ = **28**

c) **What percentage of people walk to school?**

1. Look at the 'Walk' bar. 7 people out of the total of 28 said 'walk'. Write this as a fraction. $\frac{7}{28}$ of people walk

2. Divide the top number by the bottom number and multiply by 100. $(7 \div 28) \times 100 =$ **25%**

Exercise 3

1 Alice records the different eye colours of people in her class in a frequency table. Copy and complete the bar chart using the information from the frequency table.

Eye Colour	Frequency
Blue	8
Brown	9
Green	2
Grey	3
Hazel	4

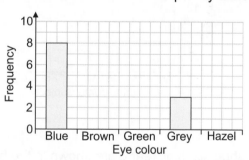

2 Fraser records the different types of DVDs he owns. The results are in the frequency table. Draw a bar chart to show this information.

DVD	Action	Comedy	Horror	Rom Com
Frequency	6	8	4	2

3   Chris records in a frequency table how many cars are in a 4-space car park at 9 am over 74 days. Copy the bar-line chart and use the frequency table to complete it.

Cars	Frequency
0	18
1	14
2	15
3	8
4	19

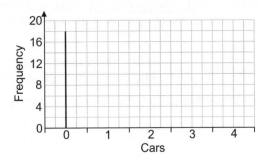

4   A cinema recorded the snacks that were sold one evening.
The results are in the frequency table. Draw a bar chart to show this information.

Snack	Popcorn	Hotdog	Crisps	Chocolate	Fudge
Frequency	17	9	13	20	6

5   Leah asks the people in her year what their favourite subject is and draws a bar chart to show her results. Use the bar chart to complete the frequency table.

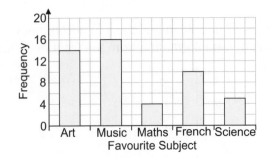

Favourite Subject	Frequency
Art	14
Music	
Maths	
French	
Science	

6   The shoe sizes of Year 8 are shown in the bar-line chart.
Use the bar-line chart to answer the following questions:

a) How many Year 8s had size 4 feet?

b) How many more Year 8s had size 5 feet than size 3 feet?

c) What is the most common shoe size for the Year 8s?

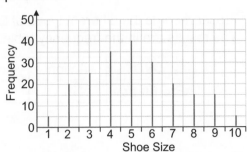

Dual Bar Charts

A <u>dual bar chart</u> shows the same categories for two different people or things.

Example 4 Sophie and Dave recorded how many cups of tea they drank
at work each day for a week. Their results are in the table.

Day	Mon	Tues	Wed	Thur	Fri
Cups drunk by Dave	3	5	4	7	6
Cups drunk by Sophie	4	0	5	6	5

a) Draw a dual bar chart to show this data.

1. Each day will have two bars — one
   for Dave and one for Sophie.

2. Use different colours or shades for Dave
   and Sophie's bars, and include a key to
   show which is which.

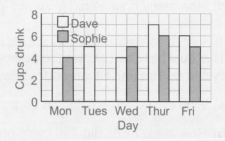

b) What fraction of the total cups of tea does Dave drink?
   Give your answer in its simplest form.

1. Calculate the total cups drunk by Dave
   and the total cups of tea drunk altogether.

$$3 + 5 + 4 + 7 + 6 = 25$$
$$25 + 4 + 5 + 6 + 5 = 45$$

2. Write these numbers as a fraction,
   with Dave's total as the numerator.
   Simplify the fraction as much as possible.

$$\frac{25}{45} = \frac{5}{9}$$

Exercise 4

1 The table shows the number of times a group of children visited an ice-rink in the last year.
No one visited the ice-rink more than 4 times.
Copy and complete the dual bar chart to show this information.

Number of Visits	Girls	Boys
0	4	8
1	8	6
2	5	2
3	3	1
4	1	0

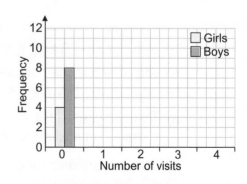

2 This dual bar chart shows the number of houses sold by two different estate agents, Frieda and Mike, over four months.

a) How many houses did Frieda sell in April?

b) In which months did Mike sell more houses than Frieda?

c) How many more houses did Frieda sell than Mike in March?

d) How many houses did Mike sell in total?

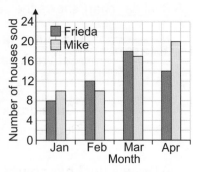

3 This dual bar chart shows the number of miles cycled by Tim and Stuart on four days.

a) Who cycled more miles on Friday?

b) How many miles did Tim cycle on Sunday?

c) How many more miles did Stuart cycle than Tim on Saturday?

d) Who cycled the most miles in total?

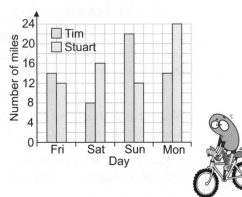

4 The table shows the test scores of the boys and girls in a class.

Marks	0-10	11-20	21-30	31-40	41-50
Girls	0	4	6	7	8
Boys	1	2	9	7	6

a) Draw a dual bar chart to show this information.
   Use different coloured bars for 'boys' and 'girls'.

b) What percentage of boys scored 21 marks or more?

c) Did the girls do better than the boys in the test? Use the graph to explain your answer.

> **Investigate — Bar Charts**
>
> A composite bar chart shows two different bits of data on the same bar, like in this example.
>
> a) When do you think it would be useful to use a composite bar chart?
>
> b) Collect some data for one of your ideas, and draw a composite bar chart to display it.
>
>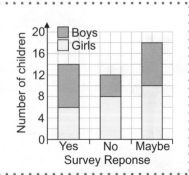

Pictograms

Pictograms show frequency using symbols or pictures instead of bars.
They always have a key to tell you what each symbol represents.

Example 5 **The pictogram shows how many apples Pete ate in 2 weeks.**

Week 1	🍎 🍎 🍎 🍎 🍎 🍎
Week 2	🍎 🍎 🍎

Key: 🍎 = 2 apples

a) How many apples did Pete eat in Week 1?

1. Count the symbols in the row for Week 1.   5.5 apple symbols

2. The key shows that each symbol represents 2 apples,
   so use this to find how many he ate.   5.5 × 2 = **11 apples**

b) Pete ate 7 apples in Week 3. Add this to a new row on the pictogram.

1. Work out how many symbols you   7 ÷ 2 = 3.5
   need to draw.
                                      So 3.5 symbols are needed.

2. Add a new row to the pictogram.

Week 3	🍎 🍎 🍎 🍎

Exercise 5

1 This table shows how many t-shirts
Ghassan bought in three months.

Month	Jan	Feb	Mar
Number of t-shirts	8	7	4

Use the table to copy and complete the pictogram.

Jan	
Feb	
Mar	

Key: 👕 = 2 t-shirts

2 The number of new members in a club was recorded over four months.
The results are in this frequency table.

Month	September	October	November	December
Number of members	10	13	12	7

Draw a pictogram to show the results. Represent 2 club members using the symbol: 🧍

3 A class was asked to name their favourite sport. 12 people said tennis, 18 people said football, 9 people said rugby and 3 people said athletics. Copy and complete the pictogram to show this information.

Tennis	⊗ ⊗
Football	
Rugby	
Athletics	

Key: ⊗ = 6 people

4 The local cinema asked a group of people how many films they had watched in the last month. The results are shown in this pictogram.

0	◯
1	◯◯◯◯◯◯◖
2	◯◯◯◯
3	◯◯◯◯◯
4	◯◯◯
5	◯◯
Over 5	◖

Key: ◯ = 10 people

a) How many people had watched 1 film?

b) How many had watched 3 films or fewer?

c) How many had watched 4 films or more?

d) What fraction of the people had watched 3 films?

5 This pictogram shows the number of bags of different colours that Jess owns.

a) How many bags does Jess own in total?

b) How many of her bags are black or green?

c) What percentage of her bags are black?

Green	👜 👜
Blue	👜
White	👜
Purple	👜 👜
Black	👜 👜 👜 👜

Key: 👜 = 2 bags

6 This pictogram shows the number of parcels that were delivered to the people in a street one month.

a) How many more parcels did Ralph get than Paulo?

b) Who received 8 parcels fewer than Jacob?

c) Who received $\frac{1}{5}$ of the total parcels?

d) What percentage of the parcels went to either Sasha or Helen?

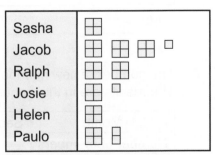

Key: ⊞ = 4 parcels

18.2 Line Graphs

Line graphs are useful for showing how something (e.g. temperature) changes over time.

Example 1 | Joanna weighs her puppy every week for 5 weeks.
She records the data in the table shown.

Age (weeks)	0	1	2	3	4	5
Weight (kg)	1.5	2.2	2.9	3.4	4.4	4.9

a) **Draw a line graph to show this data.**

1. Draw a pair of axes with age on the horizontal axis and weight on the vertical axis.

2. Plot the values from the table.

3. Join up the points with straight lines.

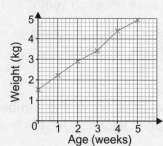

b) **Between which two consecutive weeks did the puppy's weight increase the most?**

The biggest increase is where the graph is steepest.

Between **3 weeks and 4 weeks**

Exercise 1

1 The table shows the number of points scored by a quiz team every week for 6 weeks.

Week	1	2	3	4	5	6
Points scored	45	33	38	49	35	42

Copy and complete the line graph to show this information.

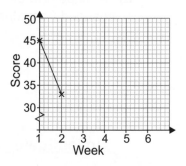

2 Samuel reads the temperature in his greenhouse every 2 hours. He records his data in the table shown.

Time	06:00	08:00	10:00	12:00	14:00	16:00	18:00
Temp. (°C)	14	16	17	24	22	20	18

a) Copy and complete the line graph to show this data.

b) Between which two consecutive times did the temperature change the least?

c) Describe how the temperature changed during the day.

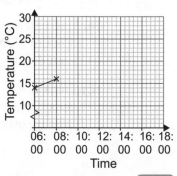

3   Terri buys a new car for £8000.
She records its value each year for 8 years,
and draws a line graph to show her information.
Use the line graph to answer the following questions:

a) How much was the car worth after 3 years?

b) How long did it take before the value dropped
below £6000?

c) By how much did its value
decrease between year 2 and year 3?

d) Between which years did its value
decrease the fastest?

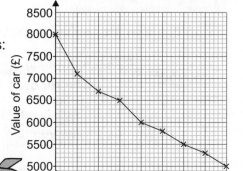

4   The line graph shows the number of visitors to a seaside resort between
March and October. Use the line graph to answer the following questions:

a) Which month had the highest number of visitors?

b) How many visitors were there in May?

c) How many more visitors were there in July
than September?

d) Describe how the number of visitors
changed from March to October.

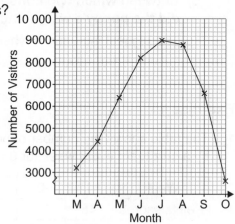

Investigate — Line Graphs

Line graphs can be used to compare
different sets of data by showing two lines
on the same graph.

a) Use this line graph to compare the
amount of rainfall in Town A and Town B
from July to December.

b) Think about other things you could compare
using line graphs. Collect some data to draw
two line graphs, then use them to compare your results.

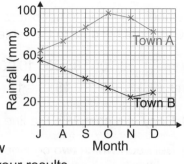

Interpreting Pie Charts

In a pie chart, the size of the angle of each sector represents frequency.
So to work out frequencies from a pie chart, you need to know the sizes of the angles.

Example 1 A student carries out a survey to find out which sport 150 students prefer to play. This pie chart shows the results.

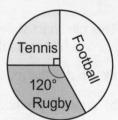

a) What is the most popular sport?

The most popular sport is the one with the biggest angle on the pie chart.

Football

b) What fraction of students prefer tennis?

1. Find the angle that represents tennis.   The angle for 'Tennis' is 90°

2. Write a fraction with this angle as the top and 360° as the bottom, then simplify.   Fraction who prefer tennis = $\dfrac{90°}{360°} = \dfrac{1}{4}$

c) How many students prefer rugby?

1. Find the fraction who prefer rugby using the angle, as before.   Fraction who prefer rugby = $\dfrac{120°}{360°} = \dfrac{1}{3}$

2. Then multiply this fraction by the total number of students. $\dfrac{1}{3} \times 150 = (1 \times 150) \div 3 = \textbf{50 students}$

Exercise 1

1 This pie chart shows the proportions of students in a class who go to different after-school clubs.

What is the most popular after-school club?

2 This pie chart shows the results of a survey about people's favourite ice cream flavour.

a) What is the most popular flavour?

b) What is the least popular flavour?

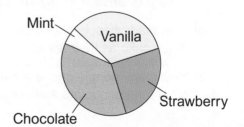

3 Heather asks 360 people about their favourite sandwich filling. This pie chart shows the results.

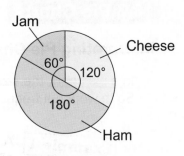

a) Which was the most popular sandwich filling?

b) What fraction of the people said jam was their favourite sandwich filling? Give your answer in its simplest form.

c) How many people said cheese was their favourite sandwich filling?

4 This pie chart shows the proportions of Ryan's class that have different pets. No one had more than one pet.

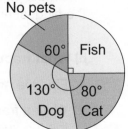

a) What is the most common pet?

b) Which is the least common pet?

c) What fraction of the class have a cat? Give your answer in its simplest form.

d) Can you tell from the pie chart how many people in Ryan's class don't have a pet? Explain your answer.

5 Katie asks 72 people what their favourite type of music is. She draws a pie chart of her results.

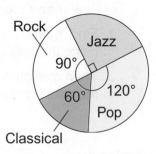

a) Which two types of music were equally popular?

b) What fraction of the people picked pop music? Give your answer in its simplest form.

c) How many of the people chose classical music?

6 Marco asks 180 people to choose their favourite type of cake. The results are shown in this pie chart.

a) What fraction of people chose lemon or vanilla cake as their favourite? Give your answer in its simplest form.

b) How many people chose coffee or toffee cake as their favourite?

c) How many people chose a cake other than chocolate as their favourite?

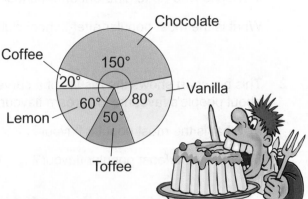

Constructing Pie Charts

Example 2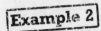

Jill asks everyone in Year 8 their favourite colour. The frequency table shows her results.

Colour	Red	Green	Blue	Pink
Frequency	20	16	28	8

Draw a pie chart to show this data.

1. Calculate the total frequency — this is the number of people in Year 8.

   Total Frequency = 20 + 16 + 28 + 8
   = 72

2. Divide 360° by the total frequency to find the number of degrees needed for each person.

   Each person represented by:
   360° ÷ 72 = 5°

3. Multiply each frequency by the number of degrees for each person.
   This tells you the angle you'll need in the pie chart for each colour.

Colour	Red	Green	Blue	Pink
Frequency	20	16	28	8
Angle	20 × 5° = 100°	16 × 5° = 80°	28 × 5° = 140°	8 × 5° = 40°

4. Draw the pie chart:
   First draw a circle, then draw a start line from the centre.
   Measure the 100° angle from here and draw another line.
   Then measure the 80° angle from this line,
   and so on until you get back to the start line.
   Remember to label the sectors on the chart.

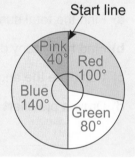

Start line

Exercise 2

1   Claire records what colour hair 36 of her classmates have.
   The results are shown in this frequency table.

Colour	Frequency
Brown	15
Blonde	17
Other	4

   a) Find how many degrees represent each person.

   b) Copy and complete this table to find the angle for each colour.

Colour	Frequency	Angle
Brown	15	15 × ...... = 150°
Blonde	17	17 × ...... = ...
Other	4	

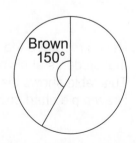

   c) Copy and complete the pie chart to show this data.

2   Boris recorded the colours of all the cars at a car show.
The results are shown in this frequency table.

Colour	Frequency
Black	8
Blue	18
Red	35
Other	11

a) Find the total number of cars at the car show.

b) Find how many degrees represent each car.

c) Copy and complete this table to find the angle for each colour.

Colour	Frequency	Angle
Black	8	8 × ...... = 40°
Blue	18	18 × ...... = ...
Red	35	
Other	11	

d) Copy and complete the pie chart to show this data.

3   A library surveyed some of its members to find out their favourite type of book.
Their results are shown in this table.

a) Find the total number of people the library asked.

b) Find how many degrees represent each person.

c) Calculate the angle for each type of book.

d) Draw a pie chart showing the results.

Type of Book	Frequency
Fiction	10
Non-Fiction	5
Picture	3

4   Ollie carried out a survey to find out how many pets the pupils in his year group have.
He recorded his data in this table.

a) Find the total frequency.

b) Calculate the angle for each number of pets.

c) Draw a pie chart showing the data.

Number of Pets	Frequency
0	36
1	22
2	10
3 or more	4

5   Hasan recorded the instruments
that students at his school play.
This table shows the results.
Draw a pie chart showing the data.

Instrument	Frequency
Flute	37
Piano	16
Recorder	50
Violin	17

18.4 Correlation

A <u>scatter graph</u> shows two things plotted against each other.

Scatter graphs can be used to show whether two things are related to each other.

If the points on a scatter graph lie close to a straight line, the data shows <u>correlation</u> — the two things are related.

A <u>positive correlation</u> means that as one thing increases the other thing increases too.

A <u>negative correlation</u> means that as one thing increases, the other thing decreases.

If the points are all spread out, the data has <u>no correlation</u> — the two things aren't related.

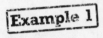 **For each of these scatter graphs, decide if it shows positive, negative or no correlation, and what that correlation means.**

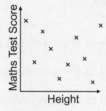

The points lie close to a straight line, and as x increases, so does y.

Positive correlation — people who are taller generally have bigger feet.

The points lie close to a straight line, and as x increases, y decreases.

Negative correlation — when daily rainfall is higher, less suncream is sold.

The points are all spread out — there's no pattern here.

No correlation — there is no relation between someone's height and their test score.

Exercise 1

1   For each of these scatter graphs, say if they show positive, negative or no correlation.

a)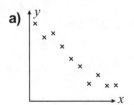

b)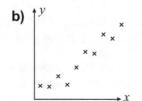

c)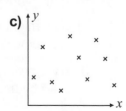

2 For each of these scatter graphs, say if they show positive, negative or no correlation, and explain what that correlation means.

a)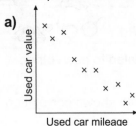

b)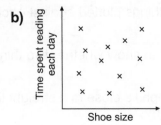

c)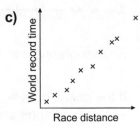

3 Match the statements **a) – e)** with the graphs **i) – iii)** to show the correlation you expect them to have. Explain your answers.

i)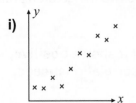

ii)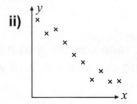

iii)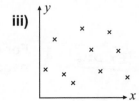

a) Shoe size and glove size.

b) Outside temperature and visitors to a theme park.

c) Wind speed and sales of newspapers.

d) Hours spent revising and score on a science test.

e) Hours watching TV per evening and hours doing homework per evening.

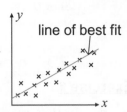

Investigate — Lines of Best Fit

A line of best fit is a straight line, drawn on a scatter graph, which lies as close as possible to as many points as possible.

line of best fit

a) How does the slope of a line of best fit compare to the pattern of the data plotted on a scatter graph?

b) Why might a line of best fit be useful for a data set with lots of points?

c) Why might a line of best fit be useful for a set of data where there are some data points that don't fit the pattern?

d) Try drawing some scatter graphs and draw lines of best fit through the data. Start by using some of the graphs from Exercise 1.

18.5 Averages and Range

Mode and Range

An <u>average</u> is a single number that represents a whole load of data.
The <u>mode</u> (or <u>modal value</u>) is a type of average. It is the most common value.
Sometimes a data set will have more than one mode, or no mode at all.

The <u>range</u> is a measure of how spread out a set of data is — it is the difference between
the highest and lowest numbers in a list. To find the range you subtract the lowest value
from the highest value.

Example 1

Harry's percentage scores in his last eight maths tests are:

79   84   75   79   71   91   89   93

a) What is his modal score?

1. It helps to put the numbers in order first.

71   75   79   79
84   89   91   93

2. The mode is the most common score.

Mode = **79%**

b) What is the range of his scores?

Subtract the lowest number (71%) from the highest number (93%) to find the range.

Range = 93% – 71% = **22%**

Exercise 1

1 Which number is the most common number in this list? 8 9 7 7 6 8 7

2 **a)** Put these numbers in order, from lowest to highest: 5 2 3 8 1 2

   b) Find the range of the list of numbers.

3 Find the mode and range for this list of numbers: 6 2 4 0 6 1

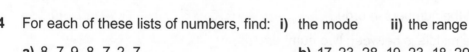

4 For each of these lists of numbers, find: **i)** the mode   **ii)** the range

   a) 8, 7, 9, 8, 7, 2, 7   **b)** 17, 23, 28, 19, 23, 18, 29

   c) 10, 1, 8, 7, 1, 9, 4, 6   **d)** 10, 11, 11, 10, 11, 10, 11, 11

   e) 46, 48, 40, 52, 59, 52, 56, 41, 57   **f)** 84, 46, 51, 55, 72, 46, 51, 57, 46, 83

   g) 98, 93, 91, 94, 81, 85, 94, 92, 90   **h)** 183, 123, 124, 105, 165, 123, 192, 104

5   This list shows the price of the same book in six different shops:

£6.99, £7.49, £6.49, £7.49, £5.99, £4.99.

What is the modal price of the book?

6   Phil records the number of people on the bus each day one week: 35, 32, 36, 30, 32

a) What is the range of the number of people on the bus over the week?

b) What is the modal number of people on the bus?

7   This list shows the number of matches in ten different boxes:

64, 62, 69, 67, 70, 65, 61, 67, 63, 71

a) What is the modal number of matches in a box?

b) What is the range of the number of matches in a box?

Median

The <u>median</u> is a type of <u>average</u>. It is the middle value in an ordered list of numbers.

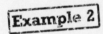   **Adam records the maximum temperature each day for a week. The results are:**
4 °C   3 °C   4 °C   5 °C   2 °C   1 °C   7 °C
Find the median temperature.

1. First put the numbers in order.

2. Then find the middle number in the list.

1   2   3   4   4   5   7

So the median is **4 °C**.

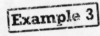   **Gemma records the number of goals she scores at six netball matches: 6   14   8   11   9   12**
Find the median.

1. Put the numbers in order.

2. The middle is between two numbers — 9 and 11.

3. The median is halfway between these two numbers. Add them together and divide by 2 to find the median.

6   8   9   11   12   14

median

(9 + 11) ÷ 2 = 20 ÷ 2 = 10

So the median is **10 goals**.

Exercise 2

1 What is the median of these numbers?

    5   7   8   9   9   11   12

2 **a)** Put this list of numbers in order:

    11   10   14   19   16   15   9

b) Write down the median.

3 Find the median for each of these lists of numbers:

a) 13, 17, 14, 11, 19

b) 42, 39, 47, 45, 37

c) 9, 35, 2, 18, 20

d) 5, 15, 7, 12, 8, 9, 6

e) 1, 2, 1, 1, 3, 2, 2

f) 27, 33, 9, 17, 30, 22, 14

g) 99, 76, 84, 91, 86

h) 106, 118, 105, 103, 115

4 **a)** Put this list of numbers in order:

    8   12   11   6   5   6

b) Write down the middle two numbers from your list.

c) Find the median of the list of numbers.

5 Find the median for each of these lists of numbers:

a) 16, 14, 12, 11

b) 2, 6, 2, 9

c) 5, 7, 8, 4, 9, 1

d) 14, 18, 16, 21, 24, 15

e) 20, 90, 50, 40, 10, 70

f) 72, 68, 54, 49

6 These are the ages of seven players on a football team: 22, 20, 23, 19, 24, 22, 18
What is the median age?

7 The number of books sold in a book shop over six days are: 96, 108, 98, 84, 102, 96
What is the median number of books sold?

Calculating the Mean

The _mean_ is a type of _average_. You find the mean by adding all the numbers in a list together and then dividing by how many numbers there are.

> **Example 4** | **Tom records how many goals he scores each month for six months. His results are: 6   9   7   9   12   8**
>
> **Work out the mean number of goals Tom scores.**
>
> 1. First add the numbers together.
>
> $6 + 9 + 7 + 9 + 12 + 8 = 51$
>
> 2. There are 6 numbers in the list, so divide by 6.
>
> $51 \div 6 = \textbf{8.5 goals}$
>
> 3. Tom can't actually score 8.5 goals — often the mean you calculate won't be a number in the list.

Exercise 3

1   a) Add together the numbers in this list: 5   4   7   3   6

    b) Find the mean of the five numbers.

2   Find the mean for each of these lists of numbers:

    a) 8, 5, 9, 2   **b)** 5, 3, 7, 1

    c) 8, 7, 11, 6   **d)** 14, 9, 13, 12

    e) 15, 11, 21, 13   **f)** 12, 10, 14, 8, 16

    g) 16, 19, 21, 13, 21   **h)** 19, 24, 23, 19, 25

    i) 20, 60, 30, 70, 80   **j)** 23, 27, 27, 18, 24, 25

3   Find the mean for each of these lists of numbers:

    a) 6, 7, 5, 8   **b)** 9, 12, 7, 10

    c) 8, 9, 7, 8, 7   **d)** 20, 24, 23, 19, 27

    e) 32, 34, 28, 31, 24   **f)** 64, 61, 65, 57, 47, 52, 56, 50

    g) 3, 4, 3, 4, 3, 4, 5, 3, 3, 4   **h)** 24, 14, 35, 34, 17, 19, 12, 9

4   The price of a bottle of lemonade in three different shops is 86p, 99p and 79p.
What is the mean price?

5   These are the ages of a group of friends: 19, 26, 24, 22, 29
What is the mean age?

6   Sara buys six potatoes. They weigh: 125 g, 147 g, 198 g, 134 g, 142 g and 154 g.
What is the mean weight?

7   These are the daily temperatures of a swimming pool over a week:

28.4 °C, 30.2 °C, 29.6 °C, 31.4 °C, 28.9 °C, 30.1 °C, 30.7 °C

What is the mean daily temperature? Give your answer to the nearest whole number.

8   Jasmine is knitting a scarf. She writes down the length of the scarf that she knits
each day: 15 cm, 19 cm, 28 cm, 21 cm, 17 cm

a) What is the mean length of knitting she does each day?

b) She knits another 14 cm of the scarf the next day.
What is the new mean length of scarf she knits?

Investigate — All the 7s

Look at the following 5 cards.

| 5 | 7 | 9 | ? | ? |

a) What digits could you put on the two '?' cards so that the range is 7?

b) What digits could you put on the two '?' cards so that the mode is 7?

c) What digits could you put on the two '?' cards so that the mean is 7?

d) Is it possible to put digits on the '?' cards so that
the mean, the mode and the range are all 7?

Comparing Averages and Range

Averages, such as the mean, can be used to compare sets of data.

The range can be used to compare the spread of two or more sets of data.

> **Example 5**
>
> **Use the following information to draw some conclusions about the heights of the girls and boys in Class 1.**
>
> The boys in Class 1 have: a mean height of 154 cm.
>   a range of 33 cm.
>
> The girls in Class 1 have: a mean height of 147 cm.
>   a range of 53 cm.
>
> 1. Compare the mean heights.
>   The mean height for the boys is larger than the mean height for the girls.
>   This suggests that the **boys are taller than the girls**.
>
> 2. Compare the range of heights.
>   The range of boys' heights is smaller than the range of girls' heights.
>   This means that the **boys' heights are more consistent**.

Exercise 4

1   The median shoe size of boys in a class is 7, but for the girls the median is 5.
       What does this suggest about the boys' shoe size compared with the girls'?

2   The temperatures in Bouth and Wick are measured every day for one month.
       The mean temperature in Bouth is 17 °C and the mean temperature in Wick is 29 °C.
       What conclusion can you draw from the mean values?

3   Two teams took part in a table tennis competition. They recorded how many points each
       team member scored. The range of points for the red team is 16 points. The range of
       points for the blue team is 3 points. What conclusion can you draw from this?

4   Alice weighs 20 dogs and 20 cats.
       The mean weight for the dogs is 32 kg and the mean weight for the cats is 4 kg.
       The range in weights for the dogs is 45 kg and the range in weights for the cats is 0.5 kg.
       State **two** conclusions that you can draw from this information.

Glossary

12-hour clock

A way of giving times. 12-hour clock times are followed by 'am' or 'pm' to show whether times are before or after 12 noon.

24-hour clock

A way of giving times. Times from 00:00 to 11:59 are before 12 noon and times from 12:00 to 23:59 are after 12 noon.

3D Shapes

Solid shapes with length, width and height.

Addition

Finding the sum when two or more numbers are combined.

Approximation

A number that is not exact because it has been rounded or estimated.

Area

The space inside a 2D shape.

Average

A measure of the most typical value in a set of data. Mean, median and mode are types of average.

Bar Chart

A chart where the height of the bars shows the frequency of each category.

Bar-line Chart

A chart where the height of the lines shows the frequency of each category.

BODMAS

A way of describing the order that operations should be done in a calculation.

Brackets

Symbols, such as (), [] or {}, used to group things together.

Cancelling Down

Dividing every number in a fraction or ratio by the same number to reduce it to a simpler form.

Centre of Enlargement

The point where an enlargement is measured from.

Centre of Rotation

The point an object turns about in a rotation.

Certain

Will definitely happen.

Coefficient

A number placed before a variable in an expression.

Common Denominator

Fractions have a common denominator when their denominators are the same.

Common Factor

A number that divides exactly into two or more different numbers.

Common Multiple

A number that appears in the times table of two or more different numbers.

Composite Shape

A shape made up of two or more simple shapes.

Cone

A 3D shape made from a circular base and a pointed curved surface.

Conversion Factor

The number you multiply or divide by to convert between different units.

Coordinates

A pair of numbers (x, y) that describe the position of a point on a grid or set of axes, e.g. (2, 3).

Correlation

The relationship between two things, usually shown by the points on a scatter graph. Correlation can be either positive or negative.

Cube (power)

A number multiplied by itself, then by itself again, written with a little 3. E.g. $4^3 = 4 \times 4 \times 4$.

Cube (shape)

A 3D shape with 6 identical square faces.

Cuboid

A 3D shape with 3 pairs of matching rectangular faces.

Cylinder

A 3D shape with 2 circular faces joined by a curved surface.

Decimal

A number where tenths, hundredths and thousandths, etc. are written after a decimal point.

Decimal Place

The position of a digit to the right of the decimal point.

Decimal Point

A dot placed to the right of the units column in a decimal number.

Denominator

The bottom number of a fraction.

Digit

One of the values (0-9) that are used to write numbers.

Distance

How far an object has travelled.

Division

The act of sharing a number into equal parts.

Dual Bar Chart

A type of bar chart where two sets of data are plotted for each category.

Edge

Part of a 3D shape, where the faces meet.

Enlargement

Changing an object's size but keeping the shape the same.

Equal

When two quantities are the same.

Equation

Something like $x + 3 = 11$ or $y = 2x + 3$, with expressions on either side of an equals sign.

Equilateral Triangle

A triangle with three equal sides and three equal angles of 60°.

Equivalent Fractions

Fractions that are equal in size but are written differently.

Estimate

A rough guess found by using rounded numbers.

Even Chance

When something is just as likely to happen as not happen.

Event

Something that might happen that you can find a probability for.

Exchange Rate

An exchange rate shows what one currency is worth in another currency.

Expand

Multiply out brackets to remove them from an expression.

Expression

A mathematical expression uses letters to represent numbers. It does not contain an equals sign.

Face

A surface of a 3D shape.

Factor

A number that divides exactly into another number.

Factorise

Rewrite an expression by putting it in brackets with a factor on the outside.

Formula

A rule written using algebra which can be used to work out a value.

Fraction

A part of a whole, written as one number on top of another.

Frequency

How many items are in a category.

Frequency Table

A table showing how many times each value in a set of data occurs.

Gradient

The steepness of a line — a measure of how much it slopes.

Highest Common Factor (HCF)

The highest number that can be divided exactly into a set of numbers.

Horizontal

A flat line going across from left to right.

Hour

A unit of time. There are 60 minutes in 1 hour, and 24 hours in a day.

Imperial Units

A non-metric set of units for measuring, including inches, feet, yards, ounces, pounds, stones, pints and gallons.

Impossible

Has no chance of happening.

Intersecting Lines

Lines that cross at a point.

Isosceles Triangle

A triangle with two equal sides and two equal angles.

Key

An instruction for reading a diagram or graph.

Kite

A quadrilateral with two pairs of equal sides and one pair of equal angles.

Like Terms

Terms that contain the same letters.

Line Graph

A graph showing two things plotted against each other, usually something against time. The plotted points are joined with straight lines.

Line of Symmetry

A mirror line where you can fold a shape so that both halves match up exactly.

Lowest Common Multiple (LCM)

The smallest number that's in the times tables of a group of numbers.

Map

An accurate drawing showing large distances on a smaller scale.

Mean

The average of a set of data, found by adding up all of the values and dividing by the number of values.

Median

The middle value when you put a set of data in size order.

Metric Units

A standard set of units for measuring, including mm, cm, m, km, g, kg, tonnes, ml and litres.

Minute

A unit of time. There are 60 seconds in 1 minute, and 60 minutes in 1 hour.

Mirror Line

The line that a shape or object is reflected in.

Mode (or Modal Value)

The most common value in a set of data.

Multiple

A value in a number's times table.

Multiplication

The act of multiplying numbers together.

Negative

Any number less than zero.

Negative Correlation

As one thing on a scatter graph increases, the other decreases.

No Correlation

The points plotted on a scatter graph are spread out and show no relation.

Number Line

A numbered scale that can be used for calculations.

Numerator

The top number of a fraction.

Operation

Something you do to one or more numbers, such as add, subtract, multiply or divide.

Order of Rotational Symmetry

The number of positions you can rotate a shape into so that it looks the same.

Origin

The point with coordinates (0, 0) on a graph. It's where the axes cross.

Outcome

A possible result of a probability trial.

Parallel Lines

Lines that are always the same distance apart and never meet.

Parallelogram

A quadrilateral with two pairs of equal parallel sides and two pairs of equal angles.

Percentage

'Per cent' means 'out of 100'. Percentage shows an amount as a number out of 100.

Perimeter

The total distance around the outside of a shape.

Pictogram

A type of chart where frequency is represented by symbols or pictures.

Pie Chart

A chart where the angles of each sector are proportional to the frequency of each category.

Positive

Any number greater than zero.

Positive Correlation

As one thing on a scatter graph increases, so does the other.

Prime Number

A number that has no factors except itself and 1.

Prism

A 3D shape which is the same size and shape all the way through.

Probability

How likely it is that something will happen.

Probability Scale

A scale from 0 to 1 that can be used to show how likely it is that something will happen.

Proportion

A part of a whole. Proportions can be written as fractions, decimals or percentages.

Quadrant

A quarter of a grid.

Quadrilateral

A four-sided shape.

Range

The difference between the highest value and the lowest value in a set of data.

Ratio

The amount of one thing compared to another, written e.g. 2:1.

Reciprocal

You can find the reciprocal of a number by swapping the places of the numerator and denominator.

Rectangle

A quadrilateral with two pairs of equal sides and four right angles (90°).

Reflection

A transformation where a shape is flipped in a mirror line. OR A mirror image of another shape, with every point the same distance from the mirror line as in the original shape.

Regular Tetrahedron

A 3D shape whose 4 faces are identical equilateral triangles.

Rhombus

A quadrilateral with four equal sides (opposite sides are parallel) and two pairs of equal angles.

Right Angle

An angle of 90°.

Right-angled Triangle

A triangle with one angle of 90°.

Rotation

Turning an object, either clockwise or anticlockwise, through a given angle at a given point.

Rounding

Replacing a number with a similar-sized number which is easier to work with (e.g. rounding 2.13 to 2).

S

Sample Space Diagram

A table showing all the possible outcomes from a combination of two or more trials.

Scale

The numbers on a map or plan that show how actual distances will be represented on the map.

Scale Factor

The amount each length increases by in an enlargement.

Scalene Triangle

A triangle with all three sides and angles different.

Scatter Graph

A graph showing two things plotted against each other. The plotted points are never joined with a line, but the graph may show a line of best fit.

Second

A unit of time. There are 60 seconds in 1 minute.

Sector

A slice of a pie chart.

Sequence

A pattern of numbers or shapes that follow a certain rule.

Similar

When two objects have the same shape but different sizes.

Simplest Terms

A fraction in its simplest terms cannot be cancelled down.

Simplify

Make something simpler by dividing by common factors or collecting like terms.

Solution

The value of an unknown letter that makes an equation true. What you get when you solve an equation.

Speed

How fast an object is travelling.

Sphere

A round 3D shape which looks like a snooker ball.

Square

A quadrilateral with four equal sides and four right angles (90°).

Square (power)

A number multiplied by itself, written with a little 2. E.g. $3^2 = 3 \times 3$.

Square Root

The opposite of squaring a number.

Square-based Pyramid

A 3D shape which has a square base and 4 triangular faces meeting at a point.

Straight Line Graph

A graph where all the coordinates lie on a straight line. The points fit equations of the form $y = mx + c$.

Subtraction

Finding the difference between two numbers.

Symmetry

A shape has (line) symmetry if you can draw on a mirror line where one side of the shape is the exact reflection of the other.

Term (of an expression)

Each of the 'bits' in an expression, separated by plus or minus signs is called a term.

Term (of a sequence)

A number or shape in a sequence.

Time

How long something takes.

Times Table

Counting up in steps of a number.

Timetable

Shows the times that different modes of transport will arrive at or depart from their stops.

Transformation

Changing the size or position of an object.

Translation

Changing the position of an object by sliding it horizontally and vertically.

Trapezium

A quadrilateral with one pair of parallel sides.

Trial

An action in a probability experiment — for example, tossing a coin or picking out a card.

Triangle

A three-sided shape.

Triangular Prism

A 3D shape which has 2 triangular faces and 3 rectangular faces.

Unit

Units show what something is measured in, for example, cm, ml, kg, etc.

Unit Pricing

The cost per unit of an item (e.g. per gram), sometimes used to compare the value of things to buy.

Variable

An unknown quantity, usually shown by a letter. Variables can take different values.

Vertical

A line going straight up and down.

Vertically Opposite Angles

Opposite angles around the point where two lines cross. Vertically opposite angles are equal.

Vertex (Vertices)

A corner of a shape.

Volume

The amount of space that a 3D shape takes up.

Whole Number

A number with no digits after the decimal point.

x-axis

The horizontal axis of a graph.

y-axis

The vertical axis of a graph.

y-intercept

The point at which a graph crosses the y-axis.

Index

U

unit pricing 111-113
units 102-124

V

variables 127
vertical lines 159, 160
vertically opposite angles 175, 176
vertices 171
volume 143, 197-199

X

x-axis 152

Y

y-axis 152
y-intercept 161, 162